The Fascination of Diamonds

The Fascination of Diamonds

VICTOR ARGENZIO

DAVID McKAY COMPANY, INC.
New York

To Margaret

Second Printing, March 1966

THE FASCINATION OF DIAMONDS

Library of Congress Catalog Card Number: 65-27641

MANUFACTURED IN THE UNITED STATES OF AMERICA

VAN REES PRESS • NEW YORK

Foreword

Diamonds have fascinated me for nearly half a century. My first job was in a jewelry store—it was 1918 and I was paid $6 a week—and one of the first things I learned was how to tell genuine diamonds by sight from other white stones. Today, if you were to ask me how one does tell, I would have difficulty explaining. After a while one just "knows," the same way that an old-time prospector knows the difference between gold and iron pyrites. He would have trouble explaining, too.

In 1925, my brother Joseph and I founded the jewelry store in Denver that bears our name. Joseph bought and graded the diamonds. I had great respect for his ability, and I was content to admire the gems and sell them.

Then, some years ago, Joseph suffered a heart attack that threatened to incapacitate him. Of necessity I set about an intensive study of diamonds. I quickly realized what I had been missing. The more I learned about diamonds, the more fascinating they became.

[v]

FOREWORD

Happily, Joseph was able to return to his duties. I persuaded him to let me take part in the examining and grading. One great day he asked my opinion about a shipment of gems, and I knew that I had "arrived."

As time went on, I could not suppress a desire to tell others about the fascination of diamonds, their history, the part they play in our lives. A few published articles of mine led to requests from friends to write a book about diamonds. I know that some of them were simply being kind and tolerant of my enthusiasm, but I have taken them seriously. This year marks the fortieth anniversary of our business, and I thought this a fitting time to do so.

The buyer of a home, an automobile, or a common stock has many ways to determine the value of what he is buying. When it comes to diamonds, however, with the purchase often involving some emotional stress, the buyer seldom knows what he wants or why, and depends wholly on the knowledge and the integrity of the seller. I realize that occasionally a diamond seller takes advantage of the ignorance of the average person. Naturally, I had that in mind while writing this book. The first part has to do with diamonds in general. The second is a very simplified course in diamond knowledge designed to help you in buying—and enjoying—diamonds.

It was not easy for me to write this book, and I am indebted to many friends for their interest and assistance, and especially to my friend Bill Hosokawa for his help in preparing the manuscript. I also wish to thank those who sent me photographs, particularly my friends at N. W. Ayer & Son, Inc., who provided most of the illustrations in this book.

It is my hope that some of my love for the greatest of gems will be conveyed to my readers.

Victor Argenzio
Denver, Colorado

Contents

[vii]

CHAPTER 1

Diamond Mélange

"Better a diamond with a flaw
than a pebble without."

—*The Analects of Confucius*

Throughout the ages, diamonds have been surrounded by an aura of romance. Men have died
for this most prized of gems, and women have sold
their honor for them. Diamonds have adorned
crowned heads, ransomed kings, put starlight in the
eyes of brides—and performed some of the most demanding jobs of modern industry.

Diamonds are rare, which, together with their
incomparable hardness and brilliance, accounts for
their value as gems. They are found in only a few

parts of the world, and their origins are cloaked in mystery. Man has learned how to split the atom and explore space, but, while able to duplicate the diamond's hardness, he has not succeeded in duplicating its gemlike qualities. Yet the diamond is only a form of carbon, the common industrial material that goes into such things as rubber tires and lead pencils.

Diamonds were immortalized—not that they needed it—in a highly successful Broadway show called *Gentlemen Prefer Blondes*. In it Carol Channing, a beguiling blonde with china-blue eyes, playing the part of an eminently practical young lady, sang a little ditty that in part went like this:

> "Men grow cold as girls grow old
> And we all lose our charms in the end
> ..."But square-cut or pear-shape,
> These rocks don't lose their shape,
> Diamonds are a girl's best friend." *

She may have been right, at that. Of the million and a half American girls who marry each year, nearly 85 percent receive diamond rings as symbols of their troths. The average price paid for a diamond in this country is $225, but it is not considered

* © Copyright 1950 Consolidated Music Publishers, Inc. Used by permission. All Rights Reserved.

sporting in the best circles to ask a husband-to-be how much the ring cost until after the honeymoon. As the song indicates, diamonds do not deteriorate in value with age. In fact, they tend to be worth more over the years, which makes them a good hedge against economic inflation.

Despite their high unit value, diamonds are measured by weight—like coal or potatoes—but weight is only one of many factors involved in determining the value of diamonds. The basic unit is a *carat,* a word derived from *carob,* a small Oriental bean remarkable for its uniformity of size, which was once used in weighing gems. *Carat* is not to be confused with *karat,* which is a measure of the fineness of gold; in England and elsewhere in most British Commonwealth countries *carat* is spelled *karat* usually in reference to the weight of diamonds as well as to the fineness of gold.

A carat is 1/142nd of an avoirdupois ounce, or 200 milligrams. Although linear measure is never used to measure a diamond, it is interesting to note that a well-proportioned, properly cut one-carat diamond will measure one quarter of an inch in diameter, but an 8-carat diamond will measure only ½ inch in diameter. The average diamond sold in the United States weighs slightly less than ½ carat.

The question sometimes arises as to the origin of the word *diamond.* It comes from the Greek, *adamas,* which means indestructible. "Diamond shape" applies mostly to the shape of pips on playing cards or to a baseball diamond. It is believed that the word came from the common shape in which a diamond is found, the octahedron, whose shape resembles two pyramids fused at their bases.

The largest diamond ever found was called the Cullinan. Before it was cut, it was a fist-sized stone weighing an incredible 3,106 carats! Eight of the world's great diamonds, including the two largest cut diamonds and 96 lesser gems, were shaped from this single amazing stone. However, the vast bulk of diamonds laboriously obtained from countless tons of earth are too small or too imperfect to be classified as of gem quality and are assigned to industrial uses where their utilitarian hardness, rather than their beauty, is valued.

No one knows who was the first to discover and admire the diamond's qualities, or who, for certain, first learned the secret of cutting and polishing them to bring out their latent brilliance. Authorities seem to agree that diamonds originally were found along riverbeds in India centuries before Christ. For a long time only the wealthiest of Oriental potentates could enjoy owning diamonds.

Romantic legends quickly grew up around diamonds. Who doesn't remember Sinbad the Sailor and the Valley of Diamonds? Some of the best-known stones today have histories that rival the romance of these ancient tales.

Hardly a day goes by without diamonds making news—a theft, a fabulous collection being sold, a stone being lost down a drain or swallowed by a pet dog. As city editors will testify, almost any story involving diamonds is news.

Wholesale diamond dealers are a breed apart. Over the years they have developed a tight-knit fraternity founded on mutual respect and trust, and even though fortunes pass through their hands daily, their dealings are often almost casual. Traditionally, transactions are sealed with a simple handshake and the expression, "Good luck and blessings." These informal agreements are as binding as any written contract.

While much of the courtly ceremony has disappeared from the diamond markets, the old rules of good faith remain unchanged. The infrequent disputes between traders are brought before an arbitration panel of dealers whose judgment is final. Any dealer found guilty of dishonesty is blacklisted and automatically barred from the world's recognized trading markets.

Unfortunately, this same high sense of ethics is not always subscribed to by a few retail dealers who take advantage of the public's admiration for, but ignorance of, gemstones. Most Americans can now afford the joy of owning diamonds. Gems are sold over the counter almost as casually as rhinestones, and some dealers are scarcely more informed than the buyers. This mutual lack of knowledge can be costly to the customer.

Who buys diamonds? Almost everyone. A recent survey of diamond engagement ring sales showed that 42 percent were bought by the man alone. Another 42 percent were purchased by the man and his fiancée together. Seven percent were selected by the man with the advice of his family or a friend, but the fiancée's opinion was unsought. And a minority of girls, 4 percent, purchased the diamond themselves.

The remaining 5 percent of diamond engagement rings were selected by committee action with the man, his fiancée, his family, her family, and sometimes friends helping to make the decision. I can testify from experience that the jeweler is in for a hard time when he must wait on a committee.

In 1964 there were over 1,700,000 marriages. In over 80 percent of these, the girls received diamonds.

Incidentally, there is a legal precedent which states that when an engagement is broken, the man is entitled to the return of the ring. Back in 1947 a disillusioned suitor asked a Los Angeles court, after his fiancée broke off their engagement, to order the girl to give back a $2,500 diamond ring. Apparently there was no California law that applied, but the judge found that under ancient Roman law, going back nearly 2,000 years, the engagement ring was not considered the woman's property until the marriage took place. The Romans held that an engagement ring was a symbol of troth, and if the troth was broken the ring reverted to the donor. The plaintiff was awarded the ring, but the woman was permitted to keep other gifts of jewelry.

CHAPTER 2

Where Do Diamonds Come From?

"Twinkle, twinkle, little star,
How I wonder what you are,
Up above the world so high
Like a diamond in the sky."

—Old nursery rhyme

Although no one has ever seen diamonds being formed, we do know, for one thing, that despite the nursery rhyme quoted above, diamonds did not rain down upon the earth from outer space. It is generally agreed they were formed deep within the earth millions, perhaps billions, of years ago as the result of incredible heat and pressure being applied to form carbon. Recent experiments indicate heat in the range of at least 5,000 degrees Fahrenheit must have been required—pure iron melts at around 2,790 degrees—with pressures of more than a million pounds per square inch.

This heat and pressure could have been possible only in the seething, boiling mass of molten rock far below the earth's surface. They acted in a way that is not clear on masses of the common element, carbon.

Pure carbon is found only in two forms, diamonds and graphite. By one of those unexplainable whims of nature, one is hard, brilliant, and precious, the other soft and common. The difference lies in the arrangement of their atoms. The carbon atoms in graphite lie loosely in sheets that slide easily over each other, which is the reason graphite is often used as a lubricant.

But the carbon atoms in a diamond were stacked tightly in an orderly manner and compressed into crystalline form by enormous forces. It is this very hardness of the diamond that enables it to be pol-

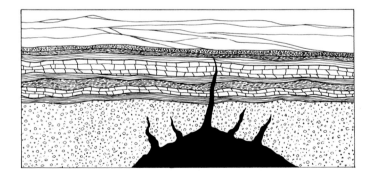

ished to a luster unequaled by any other gem.

Millions of years passed. Weak spots in the earth's crust cracked, and volcanic eruptions created mountain peaks and spewed lava over vast areas. When the molten material cooled, it formed a basic igneous rock. Kimberlite, which is the only known source-rock of diamonds, is such a rock. Then, through countless centuries, slowly but surely, the action of torrential rains, changes of temperature, the abrasion of windborne sand, the washing of rivers, and the gouging of glaciers wore the mountains down to the level of the plains. Gradually the diamonds in their beds of kimberlite were uncovered. Ancient rivers and glacial ice carried them far from their original source. Some were buried anew in stream beds. Others were washed into the sea and covered by millions of tons of debris or swept back by the waves onto beaches. The courses of rivers changed. New mountain ranges

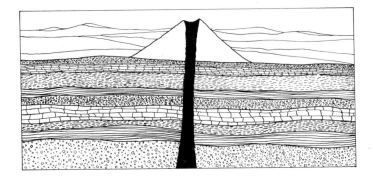

rose from later eruptions. Land masses emerged from the sea or were engulfed by the waters. The diamonds survived this merciless battering and were scattered over many areas of the world.

But in some areas, notably Africa, the roots of prehistoric volcanoes remain. These are the channels, often hundreds of feet in diameter, through which the molten masses surged to the surface. The mountain peaks have disappeared, but the lava channels still reach down into the earth. These channels are

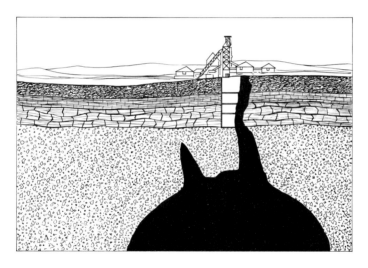

called pipes—diamond pipes—for within them is the kimberlite, the bluish rock seeded with diamonds. These pipes are among the chief sources of diamonds today. In the Kimberley area of Africa, pipe mines

[11]

follow the old channels thousands of feet into the earth.

Diamonds as produced by nature are usually shapeless pebbles. Often a "skin" hides their luster, and pits mark their surface. It is difficult for a neophyte to recognize a diamond in the rough; as one expert says, "There is no sure way to tell, you just know when you've found one." However, even the experts are sometimes fooled. Sometimes it takes intensive tests, based on the diamond's hardness, to distinguish a precious stone from a worthless bit of rock crystal. And it is only after diamonds are cut and polished that they acquire their characteristic brilliance.

The earliest record of diamonds goes back to about 800 B.C., to the stones found in India along the courses of old rivers. By 700 B.C. the gravel beds were being combed systematically for diamonds. Their trading center, Golconda, lay within a few miles of the modern city of Hyderabad. From Golconda traders carried the diamonds to Rome and Greece, and east to China. At the time of Christ, diamonds were greatly prized. Pliny the Elder, Roman philosopher of the first century, described diamonds as being so rare they were worn only by kings. He stated (erroneously) that a good way to check a diamond was to hit it with a hammer. This must have resulted in the destruction of many diamonds.

Millions of carats of diamonds were recovered from India's alluvial gravel beds. Most of them became the personal property of Indian royalty. Such famous diamonds as the Kohinoor, the Orloff, and the Great Mogul were found in India.

The next big diamond find was deep in the jungles of Brazil in the state of Minas Gerais, in 1726. Prospectors discovered quite by accident that the pretty pebbles they picked up from riverbeds to use as tallies in their gambling games were diamonds, far more valuable than the gold nuggets they had been seeking. Tejuco, the town where the discovery was made, was promptly renamed Diamantina.

When news came of Brazil's diamond find, it was received with incredulity and consternation in India and Europe. Those who owned Indian diamonds feared their value would decrease. Rumors were then spread that Brazilian diamonds were softer and inferior in quality compared to the Indian stones. When Portuguese traders encountered trouble getting their price for Brazilian gems, the stones were shipped to Goa, their colony on the southwestern coast of India. From Goa the diamonds were sent to Europe and sold as Indian products.

Actually, Brazilian diamonds are of excellent quality. Several years ago when my wife and I were visiting in Rio de Janeiro I had an opportunity to examine huge parcels of cut diamonds that had come from Minas Gerais. Many of these gems were as fine as any I had ever seen.

The Brazilian mines reached their peak of productivity in the middle of the 19th century. They are still producing, but in lesser quantities.

In 1866 a new discovery rocked the diamond world. Near Hopetown, South Africa, there lived a Boer farmer named Jacobs. One day his children, at play, picked up a bright pebble and took it home. A neighbor, one Van Niekerk, took a fancy to the stone and offered to buy it. Mrs. Jacobs laughed and gave it to him, figuring her children could find many more similar pebbles if they wanted them.

Van Niekerk wasn't sure what he had. He offered the pebble to several traders, but they were not interested. Finally a hunter and trader named O'Reilly bought it for a trifle. O'Reilly had a vague notion that the stone might be valuable, might even be a diamond, and so he took it to a Dr. W. Atherstone, an aptly named mineralogist.

Dr. Atherstone made some tests and pronounced it a genuine diamond. It weighed 21 carats and was valued at $2,500 in its uncut form. When this news seeped out, diamond dealers in London passed it off as a freak find and predicted no more than another isolated stone or two would be found in South Africa.

They couldn't have been more wrong. However, it was three years later, in 1869, before a second diamond was picked up in the area. The same Van Nie-kerk heard about it, and according to an accepted story, traded several hundred sheep, a half dozen oxen, and a horse for it. The stone weighed 83 carats, and Van Niekerk sold it for $50,000. Within another year diamonds were being found in exciting quanti-ties. Fortune hunters, including many '49ers from California, scurried into the Vaal River valley, and the big diamond rush was on.

That same year, the first of the famous South Afri-can pipe mines, the Jagersfontein, was discovered. From this mine come the famous diamonds called Jagers (pronounced Yahgers) which are known throughout the world for their excellence of color. Then came other pipe discoveries—the Dutoitspan, Bultfontein, De Beers, Kimberley, Wesselton, and many more. The Union of South Africa now began to produce diamonds in unprecedented quantities.

If the Union of South Africa had diamonds, why couldn't they also be found in adjacent lands? These countries were undeveloped, and exploration was slow. But one by one, rich new fields were discovered. Diamonds were found in South West Africa in 1908, and this area has been a major producer ever since.

The Belgian Congo, now the Republic of the Congo, yielded its first diamonds in 1916. It is presently the world's largest diamond producer, but only 5 percent of its output is of gem quality, the rest being used

The total yield of the Dutoitspan mine at Kimberley, South Africa, for a ten-day period. It includes stones of all sizes and qualities—a total of approximately 15,000 carats, both gem and industrial diamonds.

for industrial purposes. Angola, next door, has diamond-bearing areas that are really a continuation of the Congo's, but in contrast, their diamonds average more than 50 percent of gem quality. The Gold Coast, now Ghana, entered the diamond-producing picture in 1919, but unlike Angola, almost three-fourths of its production is of industrial quality.

The Sierra Leone deposits were discovered in 1930, and while more than 60 percent of the yield is of industrial quality, the gemstones are noted for their excellence. A 770-carat stone, called the Woyie River diamond, the largest ever located in an alluvial deposit, was found in Sierra Leone. This area has produced diamonds of 530 and 250 carats, and many weighing more than 50 carats.

There is an element of romance and adventure connected with the discovery of diamonds in Tanganyika, where unimportant finds had been made as early as 1910. A Canadian geologist, Dr. John T. Williamson, became convinced that huge deposits lay hidden in eastern Africa and he spent five years in a systematic search of Tanganyika, all but exhausting his financial resources. Then in 1940 at Mwadui, about a hundred miles south of Lake Victoria, Dr. Williamson's faith was rewarded by the discovery of an incredibly rich pipe mine. In area the pipe, which covers more than 250 acres of surface, is the world's largest.

More than 80 percent of the diamonds found here are of gem quality, and many unusually fine stones have been recovered. The best-known is a pink stone that weighed some 54 carats; it was cut to yield a gem weighing 23½ carats. Dr. Williamson presented it to Queen Elizabeth II as a wedding gift. Although it is relatively small, as famous diamonds go, it is one of the most valuable. Some time ago in a New York diamond cutter's stock I viewed an exquisite 19-carat rose-colored diamond from the same mine. Though smaller, it compares favorably with Queen Elizabeth's rose-colored jewel, which is a most unusual tint.

In recent years the ocean floor off the South-West Africa coast has been dredged successfully for diamonds. Some of these stones no doubt were carried out to sea by rivers and tides. However, there are rocks at the ocean bottom similar to diamond-bearing kimberlite, and it is suggested by some experts that the diamonds are products of undersea volcanic activity because the great majority of the diamonds recovered from the ocean are of gem quality, whereas those mined from the mainland are over 80 percent of industrial quality. There is also the possibility that vast areas now covered by the Atlantic were land masses at one time. Perhaps Africa and South America were once joined by land.

In support of this theory is the fact that both the east coast of South America and the west coast of Africa produce diamonds, and the geologic age of these areas is approximately the same. In addition, carbonado, an industrial diamond noted for its toughness, is found only in Brazil and Sierra Leone. (These are black diamonds without grain or cleavage, and here Pliny would have been correct—these may

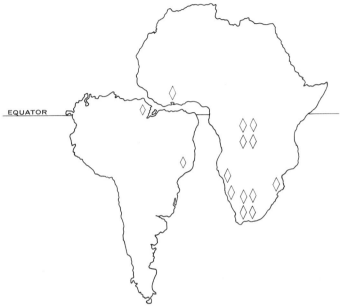

be hit with a hammer without damage.) It may be impossible to prove the land-joining theory, but it offers nonetheless an interesting subject for conjecture.

Aside from the African areas and Brazil, the only active diamond fields of any consequence are in eastern Siberia. The Soviet Union revealed that diamond pipes had been found there in 1954. The quality of these stones is not definitely known, but it is thought the majority are of industrial quality.

Some diamonds are found in British Guiana, Venezuela, Borneo, and Australia, along with a scattering

[19]

in various parts of the world, but the volume of production is negligible. The United States, rich in so many other resources, is singularly poor in diamonds, although some stones are found here.

The only American find of any consequence is near Murfreesboro, Arkansas, where there are kimberlite pipes. A 40-carat diamond was found here in 1924, and other diamonds of up to 15 carats have been recovered. However, the deposit has not justified large-scale operations.

Isolated stones, probably deposited after being carried great distances by glaciers during the Ice Age, have been picked up in California, North Carolina, Virginia, Ohio, Indiana, and Wisconsin. Most were small, but some were of gem quality.

There is at this time a scarcity of fine diamonds, and the De Beers Company have all they can do to supply the market. It seems astonishing that when the famous Indian mines became exhausted, the finds in Brazil were made. Right after the tapering off of the Brazilian mines, the tremendous discoveries were made in South Africa. Now that the South African production has reached its peak, diamonds have given up another of their well-guarded secrets and they are being recovered in quantities from the sea. It does appear that their discovery is being perpetuated for the pleasure of humanity.

CHAPTER 3

How Diamonds Are Mined

"A diamond is valuable tho' it
lie on a dunghill."

—Thomas Fuller

For a long time after Europeans learned to admire diamonds from India, their origin remained a mystery. Fantastic stories were told about caves where one had but to pick up glittering gems, of secret mountains covered with diamonds, of hidden valleys where great hoards lay.

The truth, of course, was far less romantic. Indian workmen with hand tools laboriously dug out diamond-bearing deposits from riverbeds and washed the gravel in crude placers, much as early American gold miners did.

The first authentic information of the Indian mines was brought back to Europe in the 17th century by Jean Baptiste Tavernier, a sort of latter-day French Marco Polo. He made six perilous trips into the interior of India and reported seeing as many as 50,000 men laboring in the diamond fields. Most of the mines were open pits, although he saw some tunnels bored into concentrations of ore. The gravel was hauled to a trough. Running water carried away the sand, and the heavier material—including the diamonds—remained to be sorted by hand.

Tavernier knew diamonds very well. His descriptions of the gems he bought, sold, and traded proved that his knowledge of flaws, cleavage, weights, and other aspects of a diamond's makeup was so accurate that he was instrumental in giving us the first authentic records and information on diamonds as we know them today.

In Brazil the first diamonds were recovered by prospectors who washed gravel in shallow pans. A shovel of gravel was dumped in a pan that was filled with water. With a rotary motion the prospector let the water wash away the lighter material. The diamonds, if any, remained behind.

Alluvial deposits are still being worked in many areas. A few individuals continue to mine small claims by hand, but where the yield justifies the cost, modern machinery has been put to use. In the larger

Edge of the "Big Hole" of the Premier Mine, one of the world's greatest sources of diamonds. Operations extend more than a thousand feet down. In the background are the recovery plant and the metal framework of the headgear which brings the diamond-bearing rock to the surface. The largest diamond ever discovered, the famous Cullinan, now in the British Crown Jewels, came from this mine.

operations, test bores are sunk into promising areas and the samples of gravel are studied by geologists. Huge earth-moving machines rip off the overburden, and draglines dredge up the gravel. Screening separates the diamond-bearing material, which trucks haul to plants for further treatment.

It is in the South African pipe mines, however, that the recovery of diamonds has become a highly organized operation. Five great mines are concentrated within a few miles of the city of Kimberley—the Wesselton, De Beers, Dutoitspan, Kimberley, and Bultfontein. They are referred to sometimes as the "Big Five," or as the De Beers mines, controlled by the De Beers Syndicate with headquarters in London. They produced 160 million dollars' worth of diamonds in the first six months of 1963 alone.

A vertical shaft, some thousands of feet deep, is sunk into the ground parallel to each of the diamond-bearing pipes. Depending on the geology, these shafts might be as much as a thousand feet from the pipe.

At intervals along the shaft, usually about 40 feet, horizontal tunnels are drilled into the characteristic blue kimberlite (called blue ground) which is blasted loose and trundled out in small mine cars. Elevators whisk the ore to the surface, where it is taken to the mills.

The blue ground is screened for size. The larger chunks are carried by belts to crushers to be broken into smaller pieces. Diamonds are seldom damaged by the crushers.

Water is mixed with the crushed blue ground in giant washers and stirred by metal rakes. The lighter materials are washed away, while the heavier rocks, along with the diamonds, sink to the bottom and are drawn off.

The concentrate then goes to the grease tables, which are a remarkable invention. In 1897 a De Beers engineer discovered that diamonds, for some unexplainable reason, have an affinity for grease. He found that a fast and sure way of picking diamonds out of concentrate was to use a revolving drum covered with grease which had the faculty of holding the diamonds securely while everything else was washed away.

Today's grease tables are covered with a ¼-inch layer of refined petroleum jelly. The tables are vibrated as water and concentrate are washed over them. The water carries away the dross, while the diamonds stick to the grease. The concentrate is passed over three tables to make sure that no diamonds are missed. Most are trapped before reaching the third table.

The grease is then scraped off the tables and dumped in boiling water. The diamonds are released when the grease melts and is drained away, and the precious stones are then collected for thorough clean-

Hundreds of feet underground, drillers prepare for blasting. Most miners never see a diamond in years of digging for them. Below: Still locked in the "blue ground," a diamond may be in one of the thirty-eight cars these men load in a day's work.

The rock is brought to the surface and dumped into a bin at the head of the shaft. Below: The rock is sent through a crusher that breaks it up without damage to the diamonds.

In this washer chemical floats off light waste material as heavier minerals, including diamonds, sink to the bottom. Below: The concentrate containing the diamonds is finally flushed over vibrating tables that are covered with grease.

The diamonds, with their affinity to grease, remain on the vibrating tables. Grease is scraped off, boiled to free gems. Below: Another form of diamond mining involves clearing tons of sand from rocky area in desert. Crevices in rocks are swept carefully and each pebble is examined for diamonds.

ing, sorting, and marketing. In some of the newer mills an endless belt has replaced the tables. Grease is applied to the belt and then scraped off along with the diamonds.

For some reason diamonds that have been in the sea or under water for any length of time collect a thin coating of salt, which makes them lose their affinity for grease. Diamonds that have been in water are treated with a solution of whale acid oil and caustic soda, which restores their strange affinity for grease.

The yield of volcanic pipes varies from mine to mine and, to the bitter disappointment of their operators, some may produce no diamonds at all. Over the years it has been found that the South African pipes, considered fabulously rich, produce an average of only 4½ carats of diamonds for 23 tons of blue ground. Of this yield, only about 1 carat will qualify as gems, the other 3½ carats being of industrial quality. This is about the worldwide ratio of gem to industrial diamonds.

About half of that 1 carat is lost in cutting, which leaves only a ½-carat in finished gem-quality diamonds out of 23 tons of blue ground. Put another way: for one average ½-carat diamond reaching your jeweler, 46,000 pounds of rock have been mined, crushed, sorted, washed, and picked over. No wonder diamonds are precious!

Usually pipe mines are most productive at their upper levels, the quantity decreasing the deeper one goes. Since it is probable that a major portion of the known pipes disappeared through erosion long ago, enormous amounts of diamonds must have been washed away and scattered no one knows where. Vast quantities were probably carried down to the sea.

A British engineer named Peter Keeble had his own theory about diamonds under the ocean. For reasons that were not made completely clear, he was confident that huge quantities of gems could be found off the mouth of the Orange River on Africa's southwest coast. He believed this diamond field had been there all the time, and was not the result of deposits by the river.

In 1939, matching his theory with action, he managed to bring up a few diamonds of high gem quality but could find no one willing to back him financially. Eventually he succeeded in forming a company that purchased rights to a large offshore area. A few more diamonds were recovered, but when no suitable process for dredging the bottom could be devised, the project was dropped.

Keeble returned to Britain to serve in the Royal Navy during World War II. After the war, he went from one financier to another in an unsuccessful effort to raise money for a new attempt at recovering diamonds from the ocean bottom. Even Harry Oppenheimer, chairman of the De Beers Syndicate, tried to discourage the venture as impractical.

Finally Keeble met a Texas oil production genius named Sam Collins, then living in England, who felt he could solve the technical problems of exploring the ocean floor. They joined forces, managed somehow to obtain capital, and purchased the offshore rights from Keeble's former associates. Collins designed a 160-foot barge equipped with dredging machinery and had it built at Durban, South Africa. The barge, christened Barge 77, was such an awkward-looking, top-heavy vessel that Durban authorities, doubting its seaworthiness, refused to let it leave the dock. One dark night Keeble and Collins slipped out of port with it and had it towed to their watery hunting grounds.

Courtesy of The Jewelers' Circular Keystone

Barge 77.

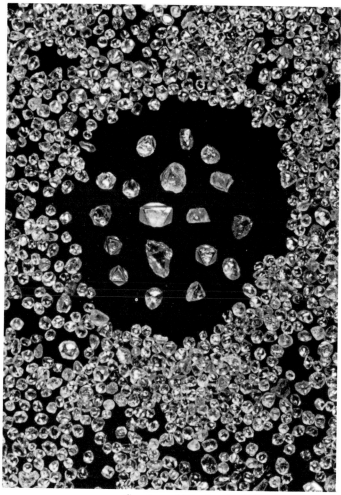

Courtesy of The Jewelers' Circular Keystone

Diamonds from the sea. (Actual size.)

The barge was anchored in 100 feet of water, where it rode out the heavy swells that had defeated earlier efforts. A compressed air hose was used to agitate the sand and mud on the ocean floor and break off bits of rock, which were sucked up in a 12-inch pipe and fed into a variety of washing jigs on the deck of the barge.

Keeble and Collins soon recovered enough diamonds to justify proceeding at full speed. They had a second barge built in Texas, sailed it to Africa under its own power, and put it to work. This operation is still going on, and several more barges are planned. In the meantime, Barge 77 was sunk during a violent storm in July of 1963. They estimate 600 million dollars waiting to be dredged up in this one area, and their goal is to recover a million carats of diamonds per annum.

The sea-dredging operations average 1 carat recovery per ton of sea gravel as compared to 1 carat of diamonds for each 20 tons average on land. These operations have attracted other interests, including Tidewater Oil. All are working harmoniously, with De Beers handling the marketing. The ocean bottom may well be the next big source of diamonds when the known fields play out. One of the remarkable aspects of the Orange River operation is that practically all the stones recovered so far are of gem quality.

With word of the Orange River find, Russian trawlers appeared on the scene. It is suspected the Russians are fishing for diamonds instead of for fish, but Collins has indicated he has nothing to worry about until the Soviets show up with barges.

Perhaps the most unusual diamond miner is a man who sits by the hour staring at the earth near Murfreesboro, Arkansas. As the sun's angle changes, he watches for tiny glitters of light on the ground. When he sees such a flash he keeps his eyes glued to the spot and directs his wife to it. Usually, it's only a reflection from a piece of bottle glass, but he is reported to have found many diamonds by this patient but rewarding method.

This piece of matrix, containing a 40-carat diamond, was recovered before passing through the crushers and illustrates how the diamond is contained in the matrix. The approximate value of the diamond is $2,800. (Photograph considerably reduced in size.)

CHAPTER 4

The Art of Diamond Cutting

"As the rough diamond from the mine
In breaking only shews its light,
Till polishing has made it shine:
Thus learning makes the the genius bright."

—Allan Ramsay in *The Gentle Shepherd*

I know of no profession more demanding than that of the diamond cutter. His hands have the skill of bringing out the latent fire and life of a nondescript stone. His ability determines whether a diamond in the rough will become just another gem, or will be transformed into a thing of awesome beauty commanding the admiration of all who behold it. Nature made the diamond, but only man can cut and polish it to reveal its hidden beauty.

Legend has it that Oriental potentates stood over

their diamond cutters as they worked, ready to order them executed if they made a faulty move. Although this was a condition hardly conducive to good workmanship, I suspect there may be a good deal of truth to this legend.

Diamond crystals as they come out of the ground are far from attractive. At best, some look like pretty pebbles. Others resemble pieces of broken glass. Some are coated with a dull film.

Diamonds as we know them today, after they have been cut and polished by modern methods, are so very beautiful that it is amazing to think that they were so sought after and prized in the days before they were cut and faceted. They must have been so eagerly desired because they were rare, and the ancients must have been fascinated by their hardness.

The cutter's job is to cut and polish the diamond to achieve maximum brilliancy, to eliminate as many flaws as possible, and to retain maximum weight.

Precise formulas for achieving greatest possible brilliancy have been worked out mathematically, and I shall go into this phase of the cutter's art in greater detail in a later chapter.

Cleaving is a very specialized art and might be compared roughly to splitting a piece of wood with a hammer and wedge. But imagine the skill necessary to work an object as hard as a diamond into the desired rough shape by splitting off unwanted fragments! Today cleaving is a dying art. More and more diamonds are shaped by sawing, although both techniques are used on some stones. Oddly enough, two of the most important cleaving jobs of all time were undertaken in this century—by the experts who cut the Cullinan and Jonker diamonds.

In the beginning, of course, the cutting and polishing of diamonds was a crude, haphazard art. Early Indian artisans rubbed two diamond crystals together with infinite patience to bring out a semipolished surface. Most of their stones were uncut, and whatever faceting was undertaken was done to eliminate noticeable flaws.

Many centuries passed before diamond cutting made significant advances. In the 13th century substantial numbers of diamonds reached Europe, where French lapidaries experimented with faceting to improve their brilliance. By 1450—forty-two years before Columbus set out for the New World—the French had achieved some symmetry of faceting. A few years later a Belgian, Louis de Berquem, who had studied diamond cutting in Paris, developed faceting to a high degree. His system was the direct forerunner of the great art of cutting and polishing as we know it today.

Basic to the art is the principle that only diamonds can cut diamonds, and powdered diamond is used to polish the stones to full brilliance. As artisans learned more and more about cutting stones, they produced more beautiful gems, with a minimum of loss in weight and size.

It might be well to explain here a few of the terms used in describing a cut and polished diamond.

A *facet,* of course, is a face or surface of the stone.

The *table* is the large, flat surface at the top of the stone. It is usually octagonal in shape.

The *girdle* is the area where the stone reaches its greatest circumference. It is from the girdle that the average stone tapers down, like a child's top, to a point called the *culet.*

The earliest standardized shape for a diamond was the "single cut." It was popularized in the 1600s by Cardinal Jules Mazarin, prime minister under Louis XIV of France, if indeed he didn't invent it. The single cut has 8 facets, plus the table, above the girdle, and 8 facets below—a total of 17 facets. The single cut is used today only for small, round stones.

Late in the 17th century, Vincent Peruzzi, a Venetian lapidary, developed the 58-facet cut that is known as the "brilliant." Nothing significant was done to improve on the brilliant until 1919, when a mathematician named Marcel Tolkowsky worked out a precise formula for angles and proportions for the brilliant to produce maximum fire and brilliance. This is known as the "American cut," or "ideal cut," and no one has been able to devise a better

The characteristic diamond shape is an octahedron, roughly like two four-sided pyramids stuck together, base to base.

The rough stone is sawed into two parts.

Next it is "rounded" by grinding the corners away.

Then, when 58 facets have been polished on the rounded stone, the result is the standard brilliant cut.

Top—33 facets   Side view   Bottom—25 facets

method since then. The term American cut refers to the syle of the cut, not to where the job was done. Thus, a stone cut in Holland may still be American cut.

Each crystal of an uncut diamond is examined minutely by the cutter for flaws and for the lines of cleavage. The obvious flaws must be removed, and the stone must be reduced to the general shape of a gem, whether it be round, rectangular, or some other shape.

Each diamond has a molecular structure that might be roughly compared to the grain in a piece of wood. Diamonds may be cleaved only along the lines of molecular "grain," so it is essential to know how the grain runs in planning the ultimate shape of the gem.

On stones of 1 carat or larger, many cutters will polish a "window" on the stone so the flaws may be located more easily. The problem is to cut the stone in such a way as to eliminate the flaws, achieve the desired shape, and still retain as much weight as possible. Even under the best conditions a brilliant-cut diamond is likely to lose half its weight before the job is finished. Once the cutter determines in what direction he intends to proceed, he marks his successive moves on the stone with India ink.

If the stone is badly shaped, or contains flaws that do not lend themselves to sawing, then cleaving is

Marking for cleaving or sawing.

called for. A large and valuable stone may have to be studied for months before the cutter is ready to cleave it.

The next step is to groove the stone so that a fine steel wedge can be inserted. This groove is made by mounting the stone on a solid base and carefully rubbing it with another diamond. Progressively sharper diamonds are used until the groove reaches the desired proportions. The blade of the wedge is held in the groove and struck with a wooden mallet or metal rod.

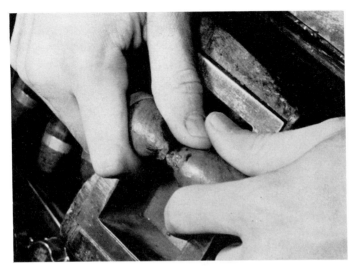

Grooving along the direction of the cleavage plane to prepare for cleaving.

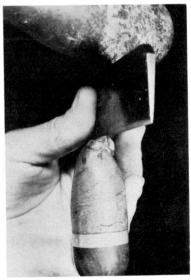

A light tap of the mallet splits the diamond in two along the natural cleavage plane.

Sawing.

Rounding.

This is an extremely critical operation. A blow that is either too hard or too soft could damage the stone. Diamonds have been known to shatter under an inexpertly directed blow. No wonder most stones are sawed!

The sawing is done by a circular blade as thin as a sheet of paper. It is impregnated with oil and diamond dust. The saw revolves at about 3,000 revolutions per minute, and the pressure of a counterweight holds the stone gently against the blade. It may take several hours to cut through a 1-carat stone.

Once the rough shape is achieved, the corners must be rounded away. The diamond is mounted on a turntable and rotated. Another roughly cut diamond, mounted on a long straight stick that is held under the operator's arm, is held against the rotating stone. Each stone wears down and shapes the other. Of course all the diamond dust and chips removed in this process are caught and saved for industrial uses.

At this stage there is still no sign of the diamond's ultimate luster. That comes in the next two steps. The blocker now takes over and gives the diamond its principal facets. The work is done on a heavy cast-iron wheel, called a "scaif." Carefully adjusted and balanced, it spins horizontally at about 3,000 revolutions per minute. A compound of diamond dust and olive oil is used to grind out the facets and the table on top, eight facets above the girdle and eight below.

Polishing.

The brillianteerer now takes over. His job is to grind the remaining facets so that, in a round, or brilliant cut, 58 facets, including the table and culet, have been attained. Today the culet (the bottom facet) is frequently eliminated, resulting in a 57-facet stone. He corrects minor errors that might have been made by the blocker, and polishes away wheel

[46]

marks. A brillianteerer must be so skilled that he can judge the all-important facet angles by eye alone. Thus the diamond emerges as a beautiful gemstone under the highly trained hands and eyes of the cutter.

Countless fine stones have been ruined by inept cutters. The most notable example is the Great Mogul diamond, which was entrusted to a Venetian cutter, Hortensio Borgio, in the 17th century. This stone weighed 787½ carats when found in India. Borgio's efforts to cut it reduced the gem to 280 carats. The Mogul Aurangzeb was so furious he not only refused to pay Borgio for his work, but fined him heavily. Borgio was fortunate not to lose his head.

The Kohinoor diamond met a similar fate in the time of Queen Victoria. It had been cut once, but when it was recut in an attempt to increase its brilliance nearly half its weight was lost. Alas, the finished product was still not a good example of the diamond cutter's art.

Belgium today is the most important diamond-cutting country, having supplanted the Netherlands. The industry also flourishes in the United States, South Africa, Britain, Israel, France, West Germany, and Puerto Rico.

The Soviet Union, under the impetus of diamond discoveries in Siberia, has been cutting stones since 1958, but the bulk of their output is sent to Britain for finishing. Israel is another country that has made

enormous progress in the last few years. Jewish artisans, many of whom migrated to Israel from diamond-cutting countries, have established modern
plants and are turning out excellent work.

Most of the largest and finest diamonds are cut in
New York, and no finer workmanship is to be found
anywhere in the world.

CHAPTER 5

Diamonds Through the Ages

"The greatest value among the objects of human
property, not merely among precious stones,
is due the diamond, for a long time known
only to kings, and even to very few of these."

—Pliny, A.D. 77

For centuries after diamonds were discovered,
only the nobility were privileged to wear them.
Someone, perhaps an early-day jeweler with profit
in mind, planted the idea among nobles that diamonds made the wearer invincible—victorious in war
and in court intrigues, safe from poison, lunacy, and
the spells of witches. Aside from such superstitions,
even the crudely cut gems of the day were treasured
mostly for their scarcity and value.

We are told that in the year 270 the Queen of Pal-

myra, a Near East domain, wore a diamond clasp at
her shoulder. However, there is scant mention in history of other women bedecking themselves with diamonds. They appear to have been largely a mascu-
line adornment. Charlemagne wore diamonds. King
Henry VIII, a man of lusty appetites, was said to
own 500 buttons set with diamonds—he may have
needed that many to keep his coat buttoned over his
enormous girth—with enough of the gems left over
to decorate his shoe buckles.

The first woman to wear diamonds as a means of
drawing attention to her own charms was probably
Agnès Sorel, a lady of the French court who had her
eye on Charles VII. The story is that she had some
borrowed diamonds made into a necklace, which she
wore to court one night. King Charles couldn't help
noticing the necklace, gasped in astonishment, and
thereafter had eyes for no one but Agnès.

This is supposed to have happened in 1444, some
years before lapidaries learned the secret of symmetrical faceting to bring out the diamond's true
beauty. Thus one may be forgiven for suspecting that
Agnès used the diamonds only to attract the king's
attention to her own charms, which were made apparent by the low-cut gowns in vogue in those days.

The noblest function of the diamond is its use as
a symbol of true love of man for maid, a token of
betrothal. This custom can be traced back to Maxi-

Imperator Cæſar Diuus Maximilianus
Pius Fælix Auguſtus

milian, Archduke of Austria, who is believed to have
been the first suitor to seal his troth with a diamond
when, in 1477, he presented one to his fiancée, Mary

of Burgundy. This act presaged a profitable marriage. Mary brought what is now part of Holland, Belgium, and Northern France under his rule.

Little wonder, then, that diamonds played a large part in the romantic fiction of Europe. Alexandre Dumas, for one, must have been fascinated by diamonds because he used them in his novels in many ways. One of his most famous characters, the Count of Monte Cristo, frequently employed his diamonds to achieve certain objectives. When the Count presented the Baroness Danglars with a pair of fine Arabian horses, each had a huge diamond placed in a rosette on its headgear.

Then there is the exciting episode in which Caderousse and his wife kill the jeweler, Joannes, after he had paid them 45,000 francs for a diamond the Count had given them—a sneaky way to recover the diamond after they had sold it. The same Caderousse, doubting that Andrea Cavalcanti's diamond was genuine, tested it by scratching a window pane. It cut the glass and proved its genuineness—a trick that cannot be recommended—and I relish his priceless remark:

"I was mistaken. But those thieves of jewelers imitate so well that it is no longer worth while to rob a jeweler's shop. It is another branch of industry paralyzed."

But even in our time the romance surrounding diamonds is very much alive. The weighing of the Aga Khan in 1946 was as fantastic as any story from the Arabian Nights. In observance of his 75th birthday a diamond jubilee was celebrated both in Bombay, India, and Dar es Salaam, Tanganyika. The value of the Aga Khan's weight in diamonds was to be contributed to his pet charities by wealthy members of the Moslem sect of which he was spiritual leader.

As princes, rajahs, and sultans watched from the sidelines, the Aga Khan deposited his 243 pounds of bulk in a brocaded, canopied swivel chair, which had been placed on a huge scale. Case after case of industrial diamonds—nearly half a million carats— loaned by the London diamond syndicate, was used to counterbalance his weight. Since industrial diamonds instead of gemstones were used, a relatively low value was placed on each carat. Even so, the value of his weight in diamonds was reported at approximately one and a half million dollars. The Aga Khan's followers contributed this amount in gold, cash, and gems, and this fortune was turned over to various worthy causes.

An interesting sidelight is that the Aga Khan was found to have lost a half pound in the second weighing, at Tanganyika. That half pound cost his charities approximately $3,500.

Today, the greatest gems are still associated with European royalty. On state occasions, fortunes in diamonds are brought forth from their vaults to dazzle viewers.

In the United States, diamonds have a somewhat more democratic role. Jewelry containing diamonds is frequently given to commemorate an anniversary, a birth, or even long and faithful service. Diamonds have also been used in advertising as symbols of superior products, and on models to sell elegant gowns.

Perhaps the most flamboyantly successful employer of diamonds for commercial gain was James Buchanan Brady, the fabulous Diamond Jim. He had a love for diamonds that became an obsession. With the purchase of his first stone he acquired tremendous pride of ownership, which bolstered his faith in himself. As he prospered, his collection of diamonds increased. He used these dazzling gems to advance his career as salesman of railroad equipment; his unique hobby enabled him to gain audiences with officials who had reputations for being difficult to approach.

Once inside the door Brady cleverly steered the conversation to diamonds, and invariably he would produce a quantity of loose stones from his wallet which he spread before the eyes of the astonished customer. Eventually he had so many he found it necessary to carry them in a belt. Diamonds were much more rare in the 1890s than they are today, and such a display rarely failed to awe the viewer and woo him into listening to Brady's dynamic sales pitch.

If anyone suggested that the diamonds were not real, which Brady hoped would happen, he would take one of the stones, stride to the nearest window, and with a flourish scratch his name on the glass. We know today there are other stones that will cut glass, but Brady's impressive act was a surefire attention getter. Diamonds became his trademark, and having a window autographed by Brady was a sort of status symbol.

Brady's unique sartorial tastes were never in much danger of being imitated. He wore a 25-carat diamond mounted in a heavy ring. His huge tiepin held an even larger stone. His enormous cufflinks were splattered with smaller diamonds. The case for his spectacles was studded with sparkling gems, and he carried a cane with a large diamond set in its ferrule. He indulged his love for diamonds to fantastic lengths, and while his flaunting of diamond wealth would be considered in extremely bad taste today, it helped make him a millionaire and a celebrity in his day.

The heavyweight boxing champion, the immortal John L. Sullivan, proudly sported his famous belt, emblematic of the championship. It had 397 diamonds.

Rather than recount the sad experiences of people

who have gotten into trouble because of diamonds, let me tell you in brief one of my favorite stories— de Maupassant's "The Necklace." It has to do with a young wife who borrowed a diamond necklace from a wealthy friend so she could go in style to a party to which she and her husband had been invited. On the way home she lost the necklace. Panic-stricken, they borrowed a huge sum of money to buy a necklace similar to the one they lost, and they handed it to their friend without explanation.

It took the couple ten years to repay the money they had borrowed, and in the meantime they suffered all manner of trials and vicissitudes for their moment of folly. Then one day our heroine encountered the lady from whom she had borrowed the necklace. In the ensuing conversation it is revealed that the borrowed necklace contained no real diamonds and it was merely one of several imitations this wealthy woman owned.

I have never forgiven de Maupassant for failing to make known whether the couple regained the diamond necklace they bought with ten years of privation.

Diamonds sometimes seem to bring out the bizarre in people, as well as the tender side of their natures. Almost any jeweler can tell stories of unusual commissions involving diamonds, and I'd like to mention a few of my own experiences.

There was, for example, the woman who sent me a snapshot of her French poodle with instructions to make a gold replica of the dog for a charm on her bracelet. She wanted a movable platinum collar around the neck, to which was to be hung a rabies tag set with a ½-carat diamond. We carried out this unusual request and gained a very happy customer.

Then there was the fisherman who landed a large trout and ordered a gold replica mounted on a miniature weighing-scale, with a triangular diamond set in the hand pointing to the impressive weight of the fish.

One of my friends once broke 100 at golf after years of patient effort. He ordered a gold tie bar in the shape of a golf club with the figure 98 encrusted in diamonds to remind him constantly of this happy event in his life.

A Denver automobile dealer presented his wife with a deluxe model car, but felt he should make his gift even more appreciated. So we set an attractive diamond ornament on the dash. Needless to say this car was never left unlocked.

Then there was the shy young man who wanted a gold calendar for his bride to wear on her charm bracelet; the date of their wedding was marked with a diamond.

Several years ago we were asked to create a large, revolving, diamond-studded star, which was to be

placed atop a huge Christmas tree on display in the lobby of a new office building celebrating its first Christmas. It was necessary to construct the star and set dozens of diamonds in it within a very few days, and this was at our busiest season of the year. It was impossible to set the stones properly in the time allotted, so we did the best we could with temporary cement. To my dismay, the star was placed close to the high ceiling, and four powerful spotlights were focused on it, creating a heat problem that could conceivably loosen the gems. But the diamonds sparkled brilliantly and stayed in place. The display turned out to be a huge success. It was mentioned in magazines, and a famous broadcaster described it on television.

Recently we were asked to come up with an idea to help publicize the local showing of Walt Disney's picture of the cat Thomasina. Our brilliant creator of unusual ideas, Louis Malucci, came up with a large replica of a cat with a 20-carat round diamond set in each eye. We were fresh out of 20-carat diamonds, so we asked the famous New York cutter, Baumgold Brothers, for the loan of two, which they graciously let us have. Valued at $150,000, the cat was probably the most heavily guarded feline on record. A local jeweler went up to the figure with his magnifier, exclaiming, "By gad, they *are* real, and fine ones too!"

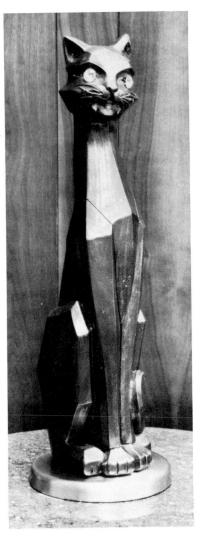

Last year, to help publicize the annual fund-raising affair of the Assistance League, a very worthy charitable organization, we made up a six-piece place setting of diamond-encrusted flatware. Set with marquise and round diamonds, and worth $5,000, it helped to attract patrons. It has subsequently been on display at a jeweler's show in New York, and it has been shown on television several times.

Like other jewelers, we have designed and executed many pieces of fine jewelry, but it is the unusual items that we remember best.

One of our most unusual pieces had to do with a customer whom I have never met, and do not expect to meet. The episode had its start over a quarter of a century ago when a lady who was a missionary came into the store. She said that she was traveling through Denver on her way home and had been asked by a native king to have us make up a piece of jewelry for him. She told me exactly what he wanted, and I arranged to have the piece made. The king had instructed that his name be engraved on the piece of jewelry. And she admonished me to be sure to have it spelled correctly. It was an unusual name, difficult to spell, and I never forgot it.

About a year later the missionary visited the store again and said the king was so delighted that he was planning to come to Denver to meet me and order additional items. "He is a big, fine-looking man," she said, "educated in Belgium, with a fluent command of French." I looked forward to meeting him, and hoped he would have an interpreter along with his retinue.

But he never came to Denver. I later learned that the Belgian colonial authorities told him to spend the money with Belgian merchants.

I had forgotten the incident about the king when, in 1962, I came across his name in a newspaper story concerning the turmoil in the Congo following the withdrawal of the Belgians. He was made the monarch of the newly independent country.

I wrote to him, extending my best wishes and reminding him of our contact in the long ago. I requested an autographed picture which he graciously sent. We decided to make him something unusual that he could wear on his person. What can a jeweler make for a king that would be unusual? Again I called on Mr. Malucci, and together we came up with the idea of a wristwatch, with a cover bearing his coat of arms set with diamonds of various colors. Special-cut diamonds were used to represent the heads of crossed spears. At the base of the cover we had engraved the national motto.

This piece was much too ostentatious for all but regal tastes, I am sure, but it was unique. This was my only association with a king. I had heard no word from him regarding the watch, but I did read that he

had kicked out the Chinese Reds who had established a foothold in his kingdom. I feel that my efforts in the regal field were on the side of freedom, at least. But I am just as happy providing standard diamond jewelry for the average person. They, too, are entitled to enjoy this gem of kings and queens.

However, all of these pale into insignificance compared to my favorite creation. It was a relatively simple gold bracelet that a young man ordered for his bride. It had seven charms attached. The first was inscribed "I love you on Sunday." Each of the others carried the same message for a different day of the week. And in each charm was set a diamond. To me, it epitomized the ageless "Romance of Diamonds."

Over the centuries diamonds have been put to beautifully sentimental as well as frivolous use, to further one's own ends or to express a selfless devotion. In each instance, diamonds said it best.

CHAPTER 6

The De Beers Story

"I beheld...an abundance of jewels..."
—Sixth Voyage of Sinbad

Diamonds are a commodity whose price is determined less by the law of supply and demand than by a single firm with worldwide influence, De Beers Consolidated Mines, Ltd.

The price you paid for your diamond was established, indirectly of course, by De Beers. The combine controlled by De Beers decides how many diamonds will be marketed, to whom they will be sold, and at what price. This, in turn, determines in a general way what the public will pay when the diamonds, cut and brilliantly polished, reach the retail jeweler.

The combine controls the industry with an iron

grip. Yet almost everyone agrees that the system is fair and necessary, and without it the diamond business could quickly find itself in a state of chaos.

The De Beers story is largely the story of Cecil John Rhodes, an intrepid Englishman. He was one of a dozen children born to a rural vicar. Sickly as a child, Cecil Rhodes, who became one of Great Britain's mightiest empire builders, was a man of enormous energy, foresight, and ambition. Oddly enough, this man whose diamonds had gladdened the hearts of millions of women never married.

Rhodes was born in Hertfordshire, England, in 1853. Suffering from tuberculosis, he went in 1870, at the age of 17, to Natal, where his brother Herbert was a cotton planter. Herbert was one of a party of Britons who discovered diamonds on the banks of the Vaal River. Cecil quickly forgot about cotton and joined his brother in the diamond fields.

Riches eluded the Rhodes brothers at first, but Cecil was not dismayed. Work in the open restored his health. When he wasn't working a claim, he sold drinking water and ice cream to the thirsty miners. There was such a demand for property at Kimberley that the fortune seekers were limited to claims only a few square feet in area. Miners sometimes dug with little regard for their neighbors' rights. Ropes, buckets, and tempers became hopelessly tangled. Mine walls fell in, and roads collapsed. Bloody gunfights over disputed claims became commonplace. Somehow, Rhodes survived the numerous hazards and learned everything he could about diamond mining.

As the more energetic miners dug deeper and deeper, they struck water, and their shafts became flooded. Rhodes, with two friends for partners, located a steam pump at Port Elizabeth and bought it for £1,000. They rented it to miners and made enough money to order more and better pumps from England.

Rhodes's profits were invested in claims, many of which were being abandoned by disappointed miners or sold for a mere pittance. One group he particularly liked was purchased from two Dutch brothers named De Beer. Before Rhodes could develop his properties, his health broke down again. This time he returned to England, where he enrolled at Oxford to study law. This higher education was to pay off handsomely in a short while.

When he returned to South Africa, he was gratified to find that his mines were producing diamonds. He used the income to acquire more holdings, either buying them outright or purchasing shares. Rhodes realized that the day of the small prospector, working his claim with pick, shovel, and bucket, was ending. He could envision a vast diamond-mining industry requiring consolidation of properties and huge capital investments. Utilizing his legal training and his powers of persuasion, he engineered a series of consolidations and mergers, increasing his own holdings with each move.

This course led to a head-on clash with another young Briton with similar ideas of expansion. He was London-born Barnett Isaacs, who was known in South Africa as Barney Barnato, a short, swarthy onetime boxer who, like Rhodes, was ambitious for wealth and power.

Barnato possessed keen judgment and remarkable trading ability. He gained a foothold in the diamond fields by shrewdly consulting geologists and acting upon their advice. After the yellow earth near the surface had been thoroughly combed for diamonds, it was the custom for miners to go on to other fields without exploring the hard blue ground that lay below. They didn't realize that the yellow soil was simply weathered blue ground, and that great riches lay hidden in the deeper formations. Barnato, on the strength of expert advice, bought up claim after claim on supposedly exhausted land near the huge pipe that made up the Kimberley mine.

Barnato's ambition was to win control of the Kimberley pipe. His opportunity came in 1881 when a miner named Stewart, who owned several claims in the very center of the pipe, decided to sell. Bidding against several others, Barnato bought the claims for the then fantastic sum of £175,000. Many of Barnato's associates were certain he was throwing his money away, but the intrepid promoter soon proved them wrong, and he also had other ideas.

Barnato was distressed to see some owners of property in the Kimberley area embroiled in a bitter diamond price war that resulted in stones being sold for less than it cost to produce them. He realized that a monopoly would be the only way to prevent this ruinous competition.

About the same time Rhodes was reaching the same conclusion—that the only way to control price fluctuation was to control production at the source.

This was during a period when the De Beers and Kimberley properties were producing virtually all the world's diamonds. Barnato would have been satisfied to win control of the Kimberley and work out a distribution plan with Rhodes. But Rhodes had other plans. He wanted undisputed control of South Africa's entire diamond industry, and he forthwith set out to find a way to bring the Kimberley into his organization.

The largest Kimberley mining firm not yet under Barnato's control was a French firm, Compagnie Française des Mines de Diamant. Rhodes began quiet negotiations for this desirable holding and was given assurances that the company's stock could be purchased for £1,400,000. Learning of this, Rhodes hurried to London, revealed his plans to his friends in the great banking house of Rothschild, and succeeded in borrowing a million pounds to help finance control of the powerful French firm.

Barnato, meanwhile, got wind of Rhodes's move and countered by offering the French firm £1,750,000. Compagnie Française thereupon abruptly halted negotiations with Rhodes.

But Rhodes wasn't ready to admit defeat. He went to see Barnato. It was the first time the two men had met. Rhodes warned Barnato that he was prepared to raise his bid as often and by as much as necessary to achieve his goal. Then, pointing out the futility of such competition, he offered Barnato a deal.

Rhodes proposed that he buy the French interests for the offering price of £1,400,000. He would then turn right around and sell the company to Barnato in return for a one-fifth interest in Barnato's company, Kimberley Central Mining. It looked like a good proposition. Barnato would get the French company, thus consolidating his hold on the Kimberley. Rhodes's one-fifth interest would pay off handsomely, but would not interfere with Barnato's control of Kimberley Central.

Barnato agreed to the deal, but he quickly discovered he had underestimated the ambitions of his adversary. Immediately after negotiations were completed, Rhodes began offering fantastically high prices for shares of Kimberley Central on the open market. Even Barnato's friends could not resist such offers and sold their shares to Rhodes.

In 1888 Barnato finally gave up the battle. Rhodes dictated the terms; a new firm would be formed, De Beers Consolidated Mines, Ltd., merging the De Beers and Kimberley interests. Barnato was given a huge block of stock and made a lifetime governor of the new company. This made Barnato very wealthy, but the terms of the agreement prevented his interference with Rhodes's control of the company. Barnato, with Rhodes's support, went on to become a member of the Cape Parliament.

Barney Barnato's colorful career came to a dramatic and untimely end when, in 1897, at the age of 45, he jumped overboard while on an ocean voyage to England. The final bell had rung on a career begun in a boxing ring and containing both the thrill of victory and the sting of defeat.

After consolidating his grip on the diamond industry, Rhodes obtained a royal charter for the British South Africa Company. It was an amazing grant, almost unlimited in scope, authorizing him to raise an army, if necessary to insure proper protection, and permitting him to expand the borders of Cape Colony virtually as far as his capabilities permitted.

The minority stockholders of Kimberley Central wanted no part of such power. They brought suit protesting the merger. The court agreed to a compromise whereby the Kimberley firm was allowed to liquidate its assets and De Beers was permitted to purchase them. De Beers issued a check for £5,338,-650, a staggering sum at the time, and the canceled check is still a prized memento of the De Beers company. That investment was to repay itself many times over.

Now Rhodes was free to proceed with his plans. He developed gold mining, extended the railroad system, subjugated tribes as prime minister, founded Rhodesia, and took part in the events that led ultimately to the Boer War between British and Dutch colonists. When he died in 1902, at the age of 49, his will granted a substantial fortune to Oxford University to establish the now famous Rhodes Scholarships. This fund enables 60 students from British Empire countries and two Americans from each of our states to undertake graduate study at Oxford.

Rhodes's successors at De Beers Consolidated Mines, Ltd., have carried out and even strengthened his policy of controlled supply. Today, the world production of diamonds has become much larger and more complex than Rhodes ever imagined, and the powerful De Beers group has been able to assimilate new companies or persuade them to become affiliated with the combine. This has meant dealing with a variety of governments and commercial interests. In each case, the De Beers executives have been able to demonstrate that diamond production and marketing can be conducted more satisfactorily, for all concerned, through their own central control.

In 1929 Sir Ernest Oppenheimer took over as chairman of De Beers. When the world depression of the early 1930s threatened the very existence of the diamond industry, it was Sir Ernest who guided it to firm financial footing. His son, Harry Oppenheimer, succeeded him as chairman. He, too, carried out the policies outlined by Cecil Rhodes, working out an extremely important agreement with the government of Tanganyika covering production from the Williamson mine, and persuading the Soviet Union to let De Beers handle sales of their diamonds outside the U.S.S.R. At this writing, the government of Tanzania is threatening to break with the De Beers group. It is the result of a campaign by the "Organization of African Unity" to boycott South Africa.

The U.S.S.R. has also adopted a policy to veer away from De Beers in sympathy with the South African boycott, but ultimately I daresay both will find it to their advantage to market through the world syndicate. The genius and foresight of Cecil John Rhodes established a solid foundation for the continuing success and growth of a great industry.

The actual marketing of most of the world's diamonds is handled now by the Diamond Producers' Association, which has its head office in Kimberley.

Rough diamonds from the various African mines arrive here daily for distribution.

Diamonds of industrial quality, which make up about 80 percent of the output, are separated and sent to Johannesburg, where they are further grouped and classified before being shipped to world markets.

The gem diamonds are carefully sorted by shape,

internal quality, and color into approximately 1,000 categories. This work is done in Kimberley, Johannesburg, and London by extremely skilled classifiers. After the stones are sorted, an organization known as the Diamond Trading Company divides the rough diamonds into parcels and offers them to large buyers at monthly "sights" in London and Johannesburg.

While buyers are simply invited to examine the parcels, in practice they seldom refuse to purchase the allotments parceled out to them. If the lots are larger than they need, or if they are overstocked in certain categories, they sell what they don't want to brokers and cutters. These secondary sales are negotiated through their own offices, through brokers in sales centers called "clubs," and elsewhere.

In addition to the London office of the Diamond Trading Company, the De Beers subsidiary that sells rough diamonds, there is another very important market in Antwerp, Belgium. Here they deal mostly in cut and polished gems.

Before World War II, Amsterdam was the headquarters for these diamonds, but most of the cutting houses moved to Antwerp after the war. Today there are more cutters in Antwerp than anywhere else, making the city a very important diamond marketing center.

Large diamond centers like New York have their

own diamond clubs where hundreds of brokers, dealers, and cutters engage in buying and selling the
products of the mines. In these clubs both rough and
cut stones change hands in the manner of any commodity exchange, with countless transactions, large
and small, being consummated on the spot.

CHAPTER 7

Working Diamonds

"None cuts a diamond but a diamond."

—Marston (and Webster) in *The Malcontent* (1604)

The industrial world as we know it today would not be possible without diamonds. They are indispensable in scores of tough, exacting, often dirty tasks demanding their unique hardness. Industrial diamonds are required for heavy duty in oil fields, for the precision imperative in scientific laboratories, for the day in and day out chores of countless factories and machine shops.

These duties are performed by the roughly 80 percent of all diamonds that fall short of gem quality.

Their total value is about equal to that of the 20 percent that qualify as gemstones. In a sense, these industrial diamonds are like ocean freighters, performing an essential but unglamorous service without fanfare while the luxury liners win the public's admiration and acclaim.

The lowest-quality diamonds, after being crushed and powdered, are used as grinding and polishing compounds and in the blades of certain kinds of saws and boring tools.

The better-quality industrial diamonds, including some gemstones, have roles in almost any industry. Carbonado, the hardest and most expensive of the industrial group, is comparatively rare, being found only, as stated in a previous chapter, in Brazil and Sierra Leone. Diamonds are used to true the surfaces of precision-grinding wheels. Tools tipped with diamonds perform close-tolerance cutting operations, such as putting the grooves around automobile pistons. Massive bits, tipped with diamonds, chew through miles of rock, deep below the surface of the earth, in search of oil deposits. Saws with diamond teeth are used to rip through granite and concrete as easily as ordinary saws cut wood.

Billions of miles of fine wire are drawn annually through diamond dies. For this purpose, a cone-shaped hole is drilled through a gem diamond that is then set in a steel or brass plate. Heavy copper

wire may be pulled through as many as 16 diamond dies of progressively smaller diameter until the wire is finer than a human hair. Some 400 tons of copper can be drawn through a diamond die into a wire fine enough to circle the world 20 times, before the die shows signs of wear. All that needs to be done then is to reshape the hole for the next larger size. When at last the stone can no longer be redrilled, it is ground to powder and put to work for other purposes.

This great demand for diamonds in industry is relatively recent. The industrial diamond output in 1939 was 5,000,000 carats; in 1964 it approximated 30,000,000 carats. Every day new uses are found for them—a natural-diamond knife for sectioning biological tissues for electron microscopic examination

—a tool to resurface bowling balls. Advances in technology and science and the need for increased precision in manufacturing processes have stepped up the use of diamonds. A shortage of industrial diamonds threatened the Allies during World War II as the arsenals of the Western world went to work on various complex weapons. When the Low Countries were overrun by the Germans, diamonds were among the first items to be rushed out to safety. Toward the end of the war, even our own little diamond field in Arkansas was worked for all it was worth.

After the war the United States continued to stockpile gem diamonds because of the scarcity of good industrial qualities. In 1960, the government auctioned diamonds, totaling 56,000 carats, which were in excess of strategic material requirements. This step had been prompted by the success attained in making synthetic diamonds that would stand up under industrial pressures.

In 1955, General Electric Company announced that, after years of experiments costing millions of dollars, its laboratories had perfected a synthetic diamond called Borazon. Some years later, a very important lawsuit came up in Pretoria, South Africa (as reported by the *Diamond News and South African Jeweller*), challenging the patents of the General Electric Company. The Transvaal and Orange Free State Chamber of Mines contested the applications on the ground that the synthesis of diamonds was an obvious process and not an invention. Another issue in point was that the Chamber of Mines disputed General Electric's claim that diamonds could be made from nondiamond carbon substances. In January of 1965, the same source reported that the General Electric Company was granted all of their applications.

At this time, De Beers is manufacturing synthetics on a commercial scale. Other firms are now producing them, and shortages of industrial diamonds should become a thing of the past.

Will the synthetic gem diamond ever compete with the natural stone? We have seen that in the industrial field it has done so, but when it comes to the gem quality it has not as yet been successfully reproduced, and this possibility is remote. There are some fields where only the real thing will do. Diamonds have been worn for centuries with pride, largely because of the romantic connotations involved. This is one instance where the synthetic gem will never replace the genuine article.

CHAPTER 8

Six Famous Diamonds

"The rarest things in the world, next to a spirit
of discernment, are diamonds and pearls."

—From the French

The endless fascination of diamonds is illustrated in the exciting histories of the great gemstones— great because of size, brilliance, or color, or all three. There are scores of gems that fall into this category, and entire books have been written about some of them. Of the six famous diamonds that have interested me most, four are from India, and the other two from South Africa. Each one has a dramatic history.

The Kohinoor

Gem historians have traced the Kohinoor back to 1304, when it was owned by the Rajah of Malwa in India. No doubt it was discovered centuries before that date, but fact cannot be separated from legend.

In 1525 the Sultan Baber, first of the Mogul Emperors, came into possession of the Kohinoor. In his memoirs Baber wrote that he received a quantity of precious stones, including the Kohinoor, after defeating the Rajah of Gwalior in battle. These gems had been owned by the Sultan Ala ed-Din, who reigned from 1288 to 1321. How Ala ed-Din gained possession of them from the Rajah of Malwa is not known.

After Baber's death the gems were passed down from each reigning Mogul to his son, including the builder of the Taj Mahal, Shah Jehan. They remained in the hands of the Moguls until India, then ruled by Mohammed Shah, was invaded by the Persians under Nadir Shah, who seized the entire jewel collection with the exception of the Kohinoor. Somehow, the Kohinoor had disappeared.

Nadir Shah was furious. He ordered a systematic search of Delhi while his men pillaged and burned, but the stone was nowhere to be found. Now Nadir Shah resorted to cunning. He had either heard the Persian equivalent of the expression of ''Cherchez la femme,'' or he invented it on the spot, and from one of the defeated Mogul's harem girls, no doubt by a promise of favors, he obtained the secret that Mohammed Shah always kept the diamond hidden in the folds of his turban.

Nadir Shah could easily have killed the Mogul and taken the diamond. Instead, Nadir arranged an elaborate ceremony at which he reinstated Mohammed Shah amid mutual promises of eternal friendship. At this point, Nadir Shah asked the Mogul to exchange turbans as a binding mark of their alliance. Mohammed Shah could not refuse without offending his conqueror. He had no opportunity to remove the diamond. Without change of expression, he gave up his turban and the Kohinoor.

It is said that when Nadir Shah withdrew to his tent, unfolded the turban, and beheld the brilliance of the coveted stone, he exclaimed, "Koh-i-noor," meaning "mountain of light" in Persian. The gem has been called that ever since.

Violence swirled around the Kohinoor for the next several centuries. Nadir Shah was assassinated, and the stone became the property of his son, Shah Rukh. In time Shah Rukh was deposed. Even though he was tortured to death, he refused to tell where he had hidden the Kohinoor. The fateful diamond was rescued by Ahmed Shah, founder of the Durani Afghan dynasty. On Rukh's death, Ahmed Shah inherited the diamond, and when he died it passed to his son,

Replicas of the Kohinoor diamond before and after re-
fashioning. The model held in the hand shows the famous
Kohinoor diamond as it appeared to Queen Victoria when
presented to her in 1850.

Timur. Timur, in turn, gave it to his eldest son, Zeman.

Shah Zeman was subsequently deposed and succeeded by his brother, Shah Shuja, who gained possession of the Kohinoor. But he didn't reign long, either.

Shah Shuja was exiled along with Zeman. The two fled to the court of Ranjit Singh, the Lion of the Punjab, taking the Kohinoor with them. Ranjit Singh, perhaps in return for granting the brothers sanctuary, took possession of the Kohinoor. He wore it in a bracelet for several years, then had it reset in an armlet, wearing the gem wherever he traveled. After Ranjit Singh died in 1739 the Kohinoor remained for an uneventful century in the treasury of the Punjab at Lahore.

In 1849, following the mutiny of the Sikh regiments which led to the annexation of the Punjab to the British Empire, the Kohinoor came into the hands of the East India Company. The following year it was presented to Queen Victoria in commemoration of the 250th anniversary of the chartering of the East India Company by Queen Elizabeth I.

The Kohinoor, cut originally by primitive Indian artisans, then weighed 186 carats. It had four grooves in it to accommodate the setting in Rajit Singh's armlet. But for all its glamorous reputation, its lack of fire left something to be desired. Queen Victoria decided to have it recut.

The foremost cutter of the time, a Hollander, was called to London for the job and installed in the workship of the royal jewelers. Prince Albert and the Duke of Wellington took part in the installation ceremonies. After 38 days of labor, the Kohinoor was presented as a 109-carat stone.

The recutting failed to accomplish its goal successfully, and the Kohinoor still leaves something to be desired in the way of brilliance, which affects its beauty. However, no other diamond has the extensive history of this famous stone, and it has an honored setting in the crown of Britain's Queen. It was worn at the coronation in 1953 of Her Majesty, Queen Elizabeth II, and is on display with the other Crown Jewels in the Tower of London.

The Regent

The Regent diamond (also called the Pitt) was found in 1701 in India by a slave. Its original weight in the rough was 410 carats. According to legend, the slave who found this stone ran away with it and gave it to a sea captain in exchange for passage to freedom. There are a number of variations to this story. One is that the captain threw the slave overboard, sold the gem to an Indian merchant for a few thousand dollars, lived riotously on the money, and then hanged himself in remorse.

At any rate, Sir Thomas Pitt, governor of Madras,

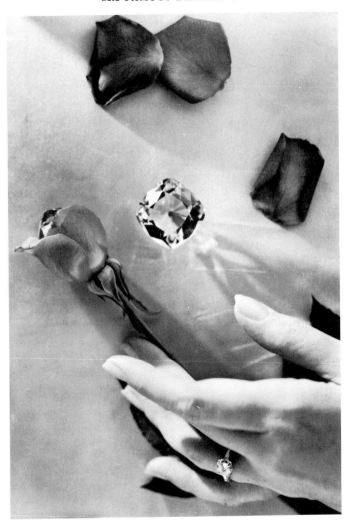

Replica of the Regent compared with diamond in engagement ring.

bought the rough diamond in 1702 for $100,000, a pretty sum in those days. Pitt was the grandfather of William Pitt, in honor of whom Pittsburgh, Pa., was named.

The stone was sent to England, where it was cut into a beautiful cushion-shaped gem weighing 140.5 carats. It is said that such a remarkable job was done that its beauty and brilliance could be no greater if it had been cut by today's skilled artisans.

In 1717 the diamond was sold to the Duke of Orleans, then Regent of France, for approximately $500,000, and thereby gained its name. The gem was placed in the crown of Louis XV. In the time of Louis XVI, when the crown jewels were worn by the royal family as personal adornments, Marie Antoinette displayed the Regent on a velvet hat.

The Regent disappeared in the famous French jewel robbery of 1792, but was recovered in a Parisian garret. In 1797, when Napoleon was making his bid for power, the Regent was pledged as security for a loan from German bankers. Five years later, Bonaparte redeemed the stone and had it mounted in the hilt of his ceremonial sword for his coronation as emperor.

After Napoleon was exiled, Empress Marie Louise carried the Regent with her to the château of Blois. Her father, Emperor Francis II of Austria, returned the diamond to the French. Charles X wore the Re-

gent for his coronation in 1852, and it remained
among the crown jewels until the time of Napoleon
III. In 1887, when France needed funds, many of the
crown jewels were auctioned, but the Regent was
held out of the sale and placed on exhibit in the
Louvre as a national treasure.

When the Germans invaded Paris in 1940, the
Regent was hidden near Chambord in the château
country. After the war, it was returned to its place
in the Louvre.

The Cullinan

On January 25, 1905, Frederick Wells, superin-
tendent, was on a routine check of the Premier Mine
in South Africa when he sighted the reflection of the
setting sun glinting off the wall of a shaft. He went
to investigate and found what seemed to be a large
crystal partly uncovered.

With a knife he dug away the ground in which it
was embedded. The more he dug, the more of the
crystal appeared. Finally he dislodged a stone as
large as a man's fist. It weighed 1⅓ pounds avoirdupois, was 3⅞ inches long, 2¼ inches wide, and 2⅝
inches high.

Wells was stunned. At first he thought someone
had played a practical joke on him by planting a
piece of glass in the mine. Before reporting the find,

he had the stone checked privately and learned that it was indeed a huge diamond, weighing 3,106 carats.

One side of the stone was smooth, leading some experts to believe the gem had been split by nature, and that it was only part of the original. The diamond—the largest ever found—was almost completely free of flaws and had a beautiful limpid color. It was named after Sir Thomas Cullinan, head of the Premier Mine. Wells received a $10,000 reward.

The way Cullinan found the mine in the first place makes an interesting story. In 1902 he found diamond-bearing gravel while prospecting on the bed of a small stream. Studying the area, Cullinan decided the diamonds had been washed down from nearby property owned by one Joachim Prinsloo, who had a reputation for distrusting diamond prospectors. He was never seen without his rifle, refused to sell his land, and allowed no strangers on his property.

Some sources say Cullinan bought Prinsloo's land for $125,000 after repeated matching of wits. Others say he waited until Prinsloo died and purchased the property from his daughter. At any rate, Cullinan's deductions were right. A kimberlite pipe was found and the Premier became one of South Africa's most productive mines.

At Prime Minister Botha's suggestion, the government of Transvaal bought the Cullinan diamond and presented it to King Edward VII of England as a token of the colony's appreciation for its newly granted constitution. The stone was presented to Edward on his 66th birthday.

The treasured stone was taken to the Asscher Brothers plant in Amsterdam for cutting. Following months of study by various experts, it was decided to cleave the fantastically huge diamond into three pieces. After further careful pondering, a groove was cut into the stone at a point which the cutter calculated was the correct line.

At 2:45 P.M., February 10, 1908, the cutter, Joseph Asscher, surrounded by a group of associates, advisers, a doctor, and two nurses, prepared to cleave the stone. If his calculations were incorrect, this priceless diamond could shatter into a million pieces. It might split along lines other than planned. The tension in the room was unbearable.

Asscher inserted a steel blade, took a deep breath and without further hesitation lifted his rod and struck the blade a sharp blow. The blade shattered, but the diamond remained intact.

Without betraying the great emotions which must have seethed within him, Asscher calmly inserted a new blade and struck it again. This time the stone split into three parts, exactly the way he wanted it. He spent several ensuing weeks in a hospital recovering from the nervous strain he had been under.

Further cleaving and sawing produced the jewels that now are part of the royal collection in the Tower of London. The Cullinan I, the world's largest dia-

The Cullinan I as it appears in the Royal Sceptre.

[92]

mond, is a pear-shaped gem 2⅛ inches long, 1¾ inches wide, and 1 inch thick at its greatest dimension. The gem weighs 530 carats, and it is set in the royal scepter.

I had read a great deal about this diamond and have a replica of it, as many jewelers do, but I could scarcely believe my eyes when I saw it for the first time in London. This great and lovely gem is truly one of the world's wonders.

The Cullinan II, weighing 317.4 carats, which makes it the second largest diamond in existence, is a beautiful cushion-shaped stone. It is set in the band of the Imperial State Crown.

Cullinan III, 94.5 carats, is a pear-shaped stone set in the finial of the Queen's Crown. In the band of the same crown rests Cullinan IV, which is a square-cut stone of 63 carats. This is the crown that also contains the Kohinoor.

Five other large diamonds were retained by the British royal family from the Cullinan for use in personal jewelry. Although the Cullinan's history is relatively short, surely it ranks high with the world's great diamonds.

The Hope (also called the Tavernier Blue)

The Hope is easily the most famous diamond in the United States. It is notable for its rare blue color.

The Hope Diamond.

The famous French gem expert, Jean Baptiste Tavernier, heard about it on one of his trips to India and found it mounted in the forehead of a statue of the god Rama Sita.

It is not known for certain how Tavernier gained possession of it. One story is that after the guardian priests refused to sell it, Tavernier and his party bound them, pried out the diamond, and fled. At any rate, there is no doubt that he appeared in the court of Louis XIV of France in 1668 with the blue gem among hundreds of others that he sold to the king.

The unusual blue diamond, called the Tavernier Blue, weighed more than 100 carats. The king's jeweler, seeking to improve its brilliance, cut it down to 67 carats, and it became the principal gem of the French crown-jewel collection, and was named the Blue Diamond of the Crown.

This fine gem was stolen along with others in the great jewel robbery of 1792. While many of the stones, including the Regent, were recovered, the Tavernier Blue was never found.

Then in 1830 a remarkable blue diamond, weighing 44½ carats, appeared on the market in London. It was immediately purchased by Sir Thomas Hope, a banker, for his wife, after whom it was named. No blue stone that large had been seen since the Tavernier, and none has been discovered since. It is now accepted as fact that this stone had been cut from the original Tavernier Blue, which was so well known that the thieves could not hope to dispose of it in its original shape. Thirty-eight years after the Tavernier Blue disappeared, however, there was no way to trace it.

The Hope diamond has always been associated with bad luck. While this may be superstition, the fact remains that Tavernier, its discoverer, was killed by a pack of wild dogs, and thus started the legend. Reputedly, the stone passed on to Marie Antoinette who died, as we all know, on the guillotine. After its reappearance as a 44½-carat stone, the Antwerp diamond merchant who had it committed suicide.

After remaining in the Hope family for many years, Mrs. Hope willed the stone to her grandson on condition that he change his name to Hope, which he did. Young Hope sold it to pay some debts, and it changed hands several times after that, with varying degrees of ill fortune attending the owners.

In 1908 the stone became the property of a Turkish sultan who in turn sold it to a French dealer. In 1911 Edward B. McLean bought it for his wife, Evalyn Walsh McLean, heiress to a mining fortune. Subsequently, her first son was killed in an auto crash; her husband, implicated in the Teapot Dome scandal, died in a mental institution; and her daughter died from an overdose of sleeping pills. In spite of this series of misfortunes, Mrs. McLean prized the diamond until her death in 1947.

The famed New York jeweler Harry Winston bought the Hope diamond in 1949 and presented it to the Smithsonian Institution in 1958, where an average of 15,000 people view it on a Sunday.

The Orloff

This diamond was first heard of about 1750. Reports from the state of Mysore in southern India told of an idol with two huge diamonds for eyes. A French grenadier, according to the most widely accepted account, deserted during the Carnatic wars in India, learned of the diamonds, professed to embrace the Hindu faith, and eventually was made guardian of the idol.

He pried one of the diamonds loose, lost his nerve before he could steal the second, and fled. He sold the stone for $10,000 to a sea captain and, according to some historians, he was then promptly drugged and dropped overboard. The skipper sold the diamond in London, and it changed hands several times before Prince Gregory Orloff purchased it in 1774.

The diamond, which is shaped like half of a small hard-boiled egg, is rose cut at the top and entirely flat at the bottom. It is ⅞ inch high, 1¼ inches wide, and 1⅜ inches long. It now weighs 199.60 carats.

[97]

A replica of the Orloff, the chief treasure of the Diamond Room in the Kremlin.

Orloff had courted Catherine the Great, Empress of Russia, but had been rejected. In an effort to gain her favor he gave her the diamond. Catherine again spurned Orloff but kept the diamond and had it mounted in the imperial scepter, where it remains to this day. Catherine had such a passion for diamonds, it is said she wore a crown set with more than 2,000 of them.

There are many historians who believe the Orloff is the same as the Great Mogul diamond. Tavernier examined the Great Mogul in Delhi in 1666 and described it as looking like half a hard boiled egg, rose cut at the top. It was alleged to have weighed 817 carats before it was cut to 280 carats. It was once owned by Shah Jehan, builder of the Taj Mahal, who also owned the Kohinoor. Tavernier is probably the only European to have seen the Great Mogul. It disappeared after the treasury was looted by Nadir Shah in 1739. It may have been recut into several smaller stones, including the Orloff, or it may have been lost. It is unlikely that anyone will ever know.

The Jonker

Jacobus Jonker, a diamond prospector for most of his 62 years, was walking on his humble farm near Pretoria after a heavy rainstorm when he spied an object on the ground. It was the size of a hen's egg and partly covered with mud.

From habit, Jonker picked it up and wiped it off. It had every appearance of a diamond in the rough and his heart almost stopped beating. Trembling with excitement, he took it home to show his wife and seven children. Of course, he couldn't be sure. He had never seen a diamond that large, and the "skin" around it made identification difficult. His wife tied it in a cloth and took it to bed with her but she didn't sleep a wink that night. Jonker and his son stood guard at the door, although no one outside the family knew anything about the stone.

Next day, January 18, 1934, Jonker took the diamond to a dealer, had it examined, found that it was indeed a diamond, and sold it for $315,000. Eventually the uncut stone was resold to Harry Winston for a reported $700,000.

After getting the opinions of the best European cutters as to how they would cleave the stone, Winston returned to the United States and sought the advice of Lazare Kaplan, a Belgian who had moved to New York. After long study, Kaplan said he would cleave it in a manner different from the way the Europeans had proposed. Winston asked him to take the job.

Kaplan hesitated. He was already famous and had a successful business. It would take months to study and cut the great stone. If his calculations proved wrong, his reputation, as well as that of American

SIX FAMOUS DIAMONDS

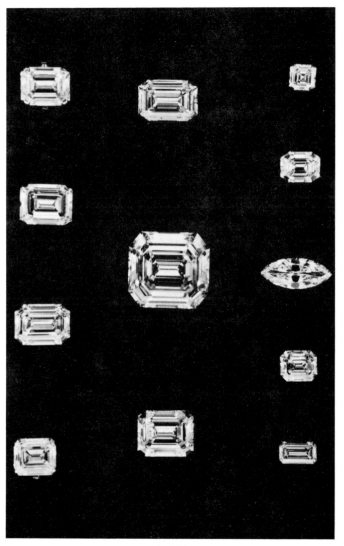

Twelve gems cut from the Jonker rough diamond. (Slightly less than actual size.)

cutters generally, would suffer. Still, the Jonker was the first large diamond to be cut in the United States and Kaplan finally accepted the challenge. Few great diamonds have been cleaved, and the responsibility resting with the cutter is tremendous.

Kaplan made models of the stone and studied them for a year. Just when he thought he had the exact spot for cleavage pinpointed, he observed a microscopic bend in a surface crack. He would have to alter his calculations and so he began his studies of the diamond's crystallization all over again.

Finally he told Winston he was ready. He said the Jonker would yield 11 emerald-cut diamonds including one very large one, plus a marquise-shaped stone. Winston told him to go ahead. After resting several days, Kaplan returned to his workshop and, with his son Leo assisting, coolly administered the tap and the diamond fell apart exactly as he had calculated.

The largest stone, 125.65 carats, was named the Jonker. It is the largest and finest emerald-cut diamond. It was purchased by King Farouk of Egypt in 1949, but later it was repossessed. Today it is the property of the Queen of Nepal, and in view of the unsettled conditions in that country on the border between Red China and India, there is no way of foretelling the future of this fine stone.

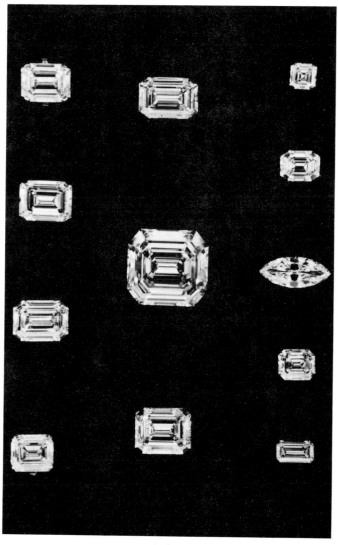

Twelve gems cut from the Jonker rough diamond. (Slightly less than actual size.)

cutters generally, would suffer. Still, the Jonker was the first large diamond to be cut in the United States and Kaplan finally accepted the challenge. Few great diamonds have been cleaved, and the responsibility resting with the cutter is tremendous.

Kaplan made models of the stone and studied them for a year. Just when he thought he had the exact spot for cleavage pinpointed, he observed a microscopic bend in a surface crack. He would have to alter his calculations and so he began his studies of the diamond's crystallization all over again.

Finally he told Winston he was ready. He said the Jonker would yield 11 emerald-cut diamonds including one very large one, plus a marquise-shaped stone. Winston told him to go ahead. After resting several days, Kaplan returned to his workshop and, with his son Leo assisting, coolly administered the tap and the diamond fell apart exactly as he had calculated.

The largest stone, 125.65 carats, was named the Jonker. It is the largest and finest emerald-cut diamond. It was purchased by King Farouk of Egypt in 1949, but later it was repossessed. Today it is the property of the Queen of Nepal, and in view of the unsettled conditions in that country on the border between Red China and India, there is no way of foretelling the future of this fine stone.

CHAPTER 9

Royal Jewels

I took a costly jewel from my neck,—
A heart it was, bound in with diamonds . . .

—Shakespeare, *II Henry VI* (Act 3)

Kings may come and kings may go, but the fascination of crown jewels goes on forever. The world today has far more crowns than kings to wear them. Yet the jewels that adorn these crowns, and other gems of royal collections, continue to intrigue the public because of their beauty, the romance associated with them, and the drama of glories long past.

This is particularly true in England where the royal family still commands love and respect, and where the state jewels are shared with the public by placing them on display. No one who has seen Britons waiting patiently in line for hours outside the famed Tower of London for an opportunity to catch a glimpse of the Crown Jewels—watched over by guards in the traditional "Beafeater" costumes—will ever underestimate the magic of diamonds.

The definitive book on royal gem collections is *Crown Jewels of Europe* by Lord Twining of Britain. It is a volume containing more than 400,000 words, 800 illustrations, and weighing 9 pounds. The subject is not one to be dismissed lightly.

Crowns of one kind or another were worn as a symbol of authority or nobility from Biblical times. The early Greeks used wreaths to crown victors of athletic events. Roman Emperor Aurelian in the 3rd century wore pearls on a ribbon tied around his head. Constantine may have been the first to use precious metal which was fashioned into a golden headband. After gold, it was just one more step to add gems, and adding precious gems was the next step in fashioning decorative crowns.

Apparently the ancient kings and queens were particular about their headpieces, much as women are fussy about their hats today. Lord Twining writes that royal personages often refused to wear crowns that had been inherited because they looked old-fashioned, were too high or too low, or fell down over the wearer's ears. So the crowns were sometimes melted down by the royal crown makers who recast the metal and embedded the gems in new designs that suited the current king's fancy.

Since it was the privilege of royalty to wear crowns, they made the most of it. There were nuptial crowns for royal brides, consecrated crowns for royal church altars, funeral and burial crowns, and even crowns which were placed on statues of monarchs. One source relates that it was the very practical Teuton, Charlemagne, who halted the wasteful practice of burying crowns and jewels with the dead. Some kings had battle crowns which they wore over their royal helmets, the idea being that the king's soldiers would recognize their leader, be inspired by his bravery, and perhaps not slay him by mistake. Of course it is possible that such a crown made the king a prime target for enemy archers.

As dynasties prospered, their collection of gems sometimes reached fantastic proportions— far greater than could be worn in crowns. These collections eventually became national treasures. The gems were acquired by purchase, as payment of tribute by conquered nations, by intrigue, and by outright plunder. Many nations and every royal family today possess gem collections the greatest value of which is represented by diamonds. In times of glory, these gems were worn by royalty on state occasions and at lavish social events. In times of stress, in more than one country, the gem treasure saved the nation from financial collapse.

The French crown jewels, for example, were valued at 30 million francs when Louis XVI in desperation ordered them sold in 1792 to support the country's shaky paper currency. Just four years prior, it had been decided that the diamonds, which had not been touched for 150 years, should be recut to conform to the cutting standards of the time. This was done, much to the consternation of the French jewelers, in Amsterdam and Antwerp.

Perhaps the world's most valuable collection of diamonds is the British Crown Jewels. Actually, it is impossible to set a dollar price on this collection, for many of the larger stones have a priceless historic and sentimental value.

These gems, while open to public viewing, are under constant surveillance. An elaborate burglar alarm system has been installed, with doors and gates being closed by remote control when an alarm is sounded. At present, a new home is planned to house what is probably the most valuable collection of ceremonial regalia in the world. More room has been requested for years, as each year visitors become more and more frustrated in their attempts to view the collection.

When I viewed this amazing collection, I was immensely impressed by the Sword of State, which has a scabbard studded with rubies, sapphires, and diamonds. It was created for the coronation of George IV. During coronation ceremonies the new sovereign presents the sword to the Archbishop of Canterbury and thus symbolizes his faith and service to the church.

By contrast to the magnificent British Crown Jewels, those of Scotland, displayed in the Crown Room in Edinburgh Castle, would be something of a letdown if one were looking only for visual glamor. Scotland's jewels yield nothing, however, in history, romance, or drama. The three main pieces are the royal crown, scepter, and state sword. These three symbols of Scottish royalty can be traced to the time of King Alexander III (1249–86) although the actual pieces are from a somewhat later period.

It was the custom in the earliest days to create new crowns for each coronation. King Alexander's regalia and jewels, most likely, were replaced after 1314 when Robert Bruce defeated the British under Edward II at Bannockburn and won Scotland its independence. Earlier Edward I of England had taken the Scottish royal jewels to England. After Bruce's victory, they were returned to Scotland, where they became affectionately known as The Honors.

Of the pieces presently on display, the scepter is the oldest. Its original, now somewhat altered, was presented to James IV in 1494. The sword of state was presented to him in 1507. The crown was made for James V in 1540, most likely from materials taken from older crowns.

Scotland's last coronation was that of Charles II in 1651. Even though Scotland has since become a part of Britain, the Scots have stubbornly retained their identity and their jewels as a reminder of the time they enjoyed their own sovereignty. Often in early times the English tried to seize The Honors, but the Scots managed to hide them.

In 1817 Sir Walter Scott received a royal warrant from King George IV of Britain to display the royal Scottish regalia in the Crown Room of the castle, and these mementos of Scotland's colorful past have remained there ever since. They are a perfect example of the contention that the value of crown jewels cannot be measured in terms of dollars alone. The pride and history of the nations with which they have been associated is reflected by the glittering gems in a way that reaches the hearts of all who view them.

Even the Communist leaders of Soviet Russia have recognized the importance of safeguarding their royal jewels for posterity. They were quick to rid the country of customs and traditions associated with the czars, but the imperial family's vast collection of jewels has been kept largely intact in the Kremlin treasury. The diamonds in this treasure total thousands of carats, and while complete details are only now coming to the attention of the public, certainly the collection must be classified as one of the world's most important.

Two pieces in the Russian treasury deserve special mention. The imperial crown, ordered for Catherine the Great in 1762, contains almost 5,000 diamonds weighing more than 2,800 carats. The second is a necklace, the main part of which consists of 36 diamonds with a total weight of 475 carats—an average of 13 carats per stone. In addition there are 15 lesser diamonds weighing almost a carat each. If the truth were known, this collection is probably one of the most fabulous gem treasures in existence.

Another immensely valuable collection is that of the Ottoman Empire on display in the Topkapi Sarayi Museum in Istanbul, Turkey. These gems were gathered during the period when Ottoman sultans extended their influence across vast stretches of Europe, Asia, and Africa, and lesser potentates paid tribute with gifts of precious stones.

I was privileged to see some of these treasures many years ago. One unusual item is a canopied throne only 7 inches high on which is seated a sultan whose body is formed by what is said to be the world's largest pearl. The turban is decorated with rows of diamonds, and in front of the throne is a diamond-studded basket filled with diamond flowers.

There are also bowls decorated with diamonds and emeralds, a flagon studded with hundreds of precious stones, and a cradle encrusted with rubies and diamonds for the pleasure of royal infants.

Iran, once called Persia, and also known as the land of the Peacock Throne, is famous for its crown jewels. The throne stands in Gulistan Palace in Tehran. Across the back are two carved peacocks, their spread tails inlaid with pearls, rubies, and emeralds. At the top is a "sun" of diamonds. Nadir Shah is believed to have brought the original seat back from Delhi after his conquest of India in 1739.

The crown jewels of Iran are not the personal property of the reigning family, but belong to the state and are used to back the currency. A treasure in loose gems, scepters, diadems, and personal jewelry is kept in heavily guarded steel vaults, each of which can be opened only by combining six keys in the custody of an equal number of guards. For affairs of state, certain jewels are made available for the queen's adornment, but they must be returned, like Cinderella's finery, after the ball.

The Americas have produced only one crown of note and it, alas, has not a single diamond in it. Still, its story is so interesting I feel it has a part in this chapter on crown jewels.

Back in 1590 an epidemic swept the west coast of South America but somehow spared the town of

Popayan in Colombia. The Catholic citizens of Popayan, believing their miraculous escape was due to
their special devotion to the Virgin Mary, commis-
sioned goldsmiths to make a crown which must ex-
ceed in beauty, grandeur, and value any other ever
made.

Where the citizens of such a small community were
able to gather such treasure is unknown, but when
the crown was finally completed after six years it
contained 450 emeralds with a total weight in excess
of 1,500 carats. The crown was offered as a token of
thanks to "Our Lady of the Andes."

In 1936 an American jeweler purchased the crown
for an unannounced sum—its value was determined
at one time to be more than $4,500,000—and reputedly
removed and sold the emeralds. Subsequently, it was
reported to have been reassembled, obviously with
different emeralds, as the price paid for it when it
was recently re-sold was just a small fraction of the
original valuation.

Many famous diamonds have been purchased by
Americans and brought to this country where they
have received the respect and admiration their
beauty and history deserved. One of the most famous
of these is the Hope diamond, and another is the
Idol's Eye, a stone which weighs more than 70 carats.
It was owned and enjoyed for many years by Mrs.
May Bonfils Stanton of Denver. It gained its name

from the legend that it once served as the eye of an idol in the Temple of Benghazi. Later, it came into the possession of Persian Prince Rahab who was forced to relinquish it in order to satisfy his debtors. At one time it was included among the Turkish crown jewels.

After Mrs. Stanton's death the Idol's Eye was sold to a Chicago dealer for $375,000, approximately half the amount its owner paid for it. Stones like this are so large that the number of potential buyers is strictly limited.

The United States, of course, officially has no crown jewels, not even a status symbol for the First Lady or a jeweled tiara for Miss America. We shall never have our history recorded by crown jewels. The countries which do possess them proudly display them. The viewer is impressed not only by their intrinsic worth, but must appreciate the historic value in their background. A student of history can well gain a new insight into the history of each nation by studying its jewels of state.

CHAPTER 10

Thieves and Smugglers

"Great wealth in compact packages tempts
the morals of even the saintly."

—Anonymous

Diamonds are small, easily hidden, and immensely valuable. There is a great demand for them. Their appearance can be altered quite readily, so that a stolen diamond can be recut and marketed with scant possibility of detection. No wonder, then, that diamond thieves and smugglers abound in fiction and pop up frequently in the headlines in real life. The strange thing is that there isn't more thievery and smuggling of diamonds, for the stakes are high and penalties are often relatively light. One observer has noted that while the value of diamonds has risen steadily, the penalty for their theft seems to remain at old levels.

The South African Parliament, in a determined effort to decrease illicit diamond buying, was recently reported to have laid down a maximum term of 15 years, plus a very heavy fine. But diamond officials admit that smuggling goes on in some areas with little decrease.

There is no accurate way, of course, to estimate the extent of illicit diamond traffic, but some authorities agree that it compares favorably with the normal trade in legitimate stones, particularly in industrial diamonds.

One well-informed source indicates that without the huge flow of diamonds that were smuggled out of Central Africa to the Soviet Union for use in manufacturing precision tools and instruments, Russia's development of the hydrogen bomb and intercontinental ballistic missiles would have been delayed many years.

Figures on Liberia's diamond trade may give you an idea of the size of this illegal traffic. Production of Liberia's own diamonds is in the neighborhood of 50,000 carats annually; yet this nation's exports are approximately one million carats each year. Most of these stones come from Sierra Leone and Ghana; a few come from other countries. This volume of trade obviously would not be possible without a highly organized distribution system.

The syndicates involved in this type of commerce continue to thrive despite the determined efforts of De Beers and other mine operators, the International Diamond Security Organization, Interpol, and the special diamond detective departments of the police in such trading centers as Johannesburg to curb this illegal practice.

Diamonds have a way of disappearing at every production stage. Sierra Leone's diamond deposits, for instance, are largely alluvial. Their stones are widely scattered in the soil as well as riverbeds, and in isolated areas the simplest of mining methods are sufficient to recover loose stones.

For years the natives turned their findings over to the firms which owned the diamond claims. In 1945, when it became apparent that East-West relations were bound to take a turn for the worse, the export of diamonds to Iron Curtain countries was prohibited. Soon after that black marketeers, knowing that buyers for the Soviet would pay premium prices, set up business in Sierra Leone and other diamond-producing countries. They corrupted the natives, the workmen in the mines and fields, and even the guards and investigators who were sent out to halt the black marketeers. At one time the world's largest producer of industrial diamonds, Société Minière de Bakwanga, in the Congo, warned that it needed government help in halting the theft of diamonds or it might have to close down its operations.

The high prices also attracted illegal prospectors. During one period the government of Sierra Leone sent 30,000 fortune seekers back to French Guinea. Since 1955 the government has been trying, with indifferent results, to restrict digging to licensed natives.

However, it takes only a few dishonest persons at each step of the diamond industry to channel an enormous amount of gems into illegitimate commerce. The rewards are so tempting that the numerous rings of diamond thieves seldom lack for willing recruits.

The smuggling chain starts with a native miner or prospector who passes the rough stones on to a black-market dealer. In the mines, there may be a fluoroscope technician who, after completing his search of a worker, hands him a can of rough diamonds that has been kept out of sight until it can safely be carried out of the plant. Then there is the mechanic who builds a secret compartment in an automobile for smuggling the stones across the border; the woman with secret pockets in her brassière; the European mine official who decides he can do better in business for himself; and the corrupt government officials, without whose help the traffic in stolen gems could not possibly be as large as it is.

In one large diamond-producing country, the government statistics fail to reflect the true output. Only a portion of the production is declared, and the balance is sold secretly by the mine operators to avoid "formalities" which is a polite word for "pay-off" to government officials. Similarly, it is a simple matter for dishonest customs officials to overlook parcels of diamonds carried on the persons or in the luggage of certain friendly gentlemen with "important" business abroad.

Perhaps the greatest gem theft of all time took place in 1792, when the French crown jewels were stolen. The culprits were never identified, although most of the jewels were found buried at the foot of a tree. This happened during a political crisis. The stones, which were valued at 30 million francs, were ordered sold to bolster the country's paper currency. The following night the gems vanished. In the turmoil which followed political factions blamed each other, and the public prosecutor even accused Marie Antoinette of having engineered the whole thing.

In the early days of the pipe mines of South Africa, native workmen were kept virtually imprisoned for long periods to make sure they didn't walk off with concealed diamonds. After working hours they were confined in walled enclosures with barred gates while armed guards watched over them. But even these drastic measures didn't stop thievery. As work contract periods neared their ends, some of the miners cut themselves in their arms or legs and secreted diamonds under their skins. Others hid stones in their hair, between their toes, in their ears, or other body cavities. Tiny stones were even stuck under their nails. Sometimes diamonds were catapulted outside the compounds at night to waiting confederates. Occasionally workmen suffering from stomach pains were found to have swallowed a handful of diamonds. Swallowing was a favorite trick until the workmen were thereafter detained for physical examinations for several days following the termination of their work periods.

Conditions are vastly improved today. Miners, notably in the De Beers operations, now have comfortable quarters, modern medical care, and an opportunity for studying and learning other trades. Bonuses are paid to miners who uncover large diamonds. Fluoroscopes and X-ray machines, while used only sparingly, help to deter temptation.

The closest I ever came to an adventure with diamond smugglers was in Egypt, many years ago, when I toured the Near East with a friend. Our ship docked at Port Said and we prepared to take the short train trip to Cairo. Since we were short of money, I took seriously a shipboard warning to beware of beggars and swindlers who preyed on tourists. As we left the ship we were handed a customs slip printed in French. I could make out only part of it, which said, "Pay nothing to the porters." I quickly assumed the steamship company had made some arrangement with them, and I thought it was a fine idea until our porters firmly and unmistakably demanded money. Equally firmly, I refused. A crowd gathered and there was much unintelligible shouting and gesticulating. Matters were rapidly becoming still more confused when a Lebanese youth, whom we had observed on the ship, came to our rescue.

In no time at all he had the situation straightened out. He explained to us that the customs slip instructed tourists to pay nothing to the porters "until they had carried the bags past a certain point." I hurriedly paid the porters. We had a good laugh and I felt much indebted to the Lebanese youth. When I told him I was a jeweler on my way to Cairo, his eyes lit up and he informed me he had a "brother" in the diamond business whom I should meet.

I'm afraid my eyebrows shot up. This sounded so much like a con game that I was instantly suspicious. However, since I had no intention of buying diamonds and I was young and eager for adventure, I told our new friend I would be happy to meet his brother. We made the arrangements, and contact was made on a busy street corner. We were led through a series of passages in one of the teeming bazaar sections and to a small shop where brassware was on display.

Our host turned out to be a nondescript character. He had two associates who stared at us in silence. After the usual small talk my host asked some pointed questions about my jewelry business, and I described my then small store at home.

It must have been apparent that I was no bigtime buyer of smuggled diamonds. He didn't bring up the subject again, although he showed me a few cut stones. However, the prices were so high it was apparent he was using them for a stall.

My Lebanese friend, obviously disappointed because he was not going to receive a commission for his pains, urged me to visit still another "brother" who, oddly enough, was also a diamond merchant. I declined the pleasure.

Stolen gems and crooked diamond cutters are a tried and true theme for many fiction writers, and they have come up with some exciting tales. One that I liked particularly well, although the author's name unhappily escapes me, has to do with Joachim, an expert cutter, who became involved with the law in his native Belgium and subsequently went to work for a gang of jewel thieves.

To escape suspicion he was instructed to take his wife, Mari, and go to New York and open a shop.

Mari, of course, knew nothing of his association with the gang. To all appearances he ran a respectable and prosperous diamond-cutting business in Manhattan, building up an excellent clientele with his courtesy and skill. However, from time to time stolen diamonds were mailed to him by the gang. There were never any instructions, but Joachim knew what he had to do. He would change the shape of one, cut down another, so that they could not be identified by their original owners. He sold these stones, retained his commission, and mailed the rest of the proceeds to the gang.

One day he received a beautiful round diamond in a shipment from Belgium. This stone had an unusual snail-shaped inclusion or flaw. It would have been perfect identification. Joachim ground the stone down until it weighed 5.07 carats, but it still had a tiny bit of the flaw left at one edge. By this time he had fallen in love with the diamond and decided to buy it for his wife. For sentiment's sake, he ground off another three-hundredths of a carat (.03) so that the stone then weighed exactly 5.04 carats. This figure had a special meaning. It represented the day he and Mari had first met—the 5th of April, following the European custom of designating the day first and then the month.

Joachim had the stone mounted in a platinum ring

and placed it on his wife's finger. She was delighted and vowed never to take it off.

Some time later Mari went back to Belgium to visit her family. Joachim never heard from her again. He knew that she was a headstrong girl, inclined to be frivolous, and he believed the worst when he heard rumors that she had taken up with a gang of jewel thieves in Europe.

The years went by, but Joachim could not forget Mari. He was sick of working with the gang and only the threat of exposure forced him to continue to do their bidding. One day he received a package from Belgium containing only three stones. The smallest one caught his eye. It was a beautiful round diamond which he estimated at about 5 carats.

Joachim wondered why it had been sent—diamonds of this size could not be traced easily in these days of soaring business in relatively large gems. Perhaps, he thought, it had an identifiable flaw which should be taken out.

He adjusted his glass to study the stone. An unusual imperfection at the edge looked frighteningly familiar. Joachim's hands trembled as he placed the stone on the scale. It weighed exactly 5.04 carats!

There are many small cutting shops and free lance cutters in a great city like New York. The owner will often rent out a wheel and bench to someone who

wants to do his own cutting. Many a stolen diamond
has been altered to escape recognition, and it is
difficult to trace these operations.

What becomes of stolen jewelry, and how do the
robbers and thieves dispose of it? Frequently after
the criminals are apprehended, sometimes on the
spot, the jewelry has disappeared. The jewelry finds
its way to "fences" without whose cooperation
jewelry robberies would lessen materially. Sometimes the stolen merchandise is shipped to foreign
countries.

When it remains here, the jewelry is broken up,
the diamonds reset in different settings, making
them almost impossible to trace. Large diamonds
which might be recognizable are altered.

Amateurs in their hurry to dispose of the loot are
usually caught easily, but the professionals who
know the ropes get their goods to fences. An experienced and successful fence sometimes owns a jewelry
store of his own, can mix the stolen diamonds with his
own stock, and can dispose of it easily.

From the level of the fences, the diamonds filter
up in different stages till they get into legitimate
channels, each time the value increasing until they
reach their true worth.

CHAPTER 11

Diamonds as an Investment

"Beauteous rubies, sparkling diamonds,
And seld-seen costly stones of great price.
This is the ware wherein consists my wealth."

—From the *Jew of Malta*, Act I

Americans are the world's greatest purchasers of diamonds. They buy them mostly for pleasure and pride of ownership. Yet it is not at all unusual for someone shopping for even a $250 diamond to inquire about its value as an investment.

This same person will pay $3,500 for an automobile which he knows will be worthless after a few years, and his chief concern is the car's appearance and how well it will perform. He'll buy a $1,000 fur coat for his wife's pleasure, knowing that it, too, will someday wear out or go out of style. Perhaps it is the very durability of the diamond that stirs the buyer's interest as to its investment possibilities.

Let's make something clear right now. Some diamonds will make a good investment for some people. But not all diamonds are a good investment for all people.

The kind of diamonds that most of us can afford and are interested in—the low and medium price diamond ring set—should not be considered an investment at all, no matter what you have been told to the contrary.

The odds are that you will not get back the money spent on a low or medium price diamond when you try to sell it. The jeweler, like any other merchant, must realize a profit on his sales if he is to remain in business. While he will usually take back a diamond he has sold you, without great sacrifice in value if you are buying a larger stone, he will be reluctant to buy it back for cash at anywhere near the amount you paid him for it.

Why should he buy it back? He has already made a profit on the original sale and you would be asking him to forfeit it for your convenience. Besides, he has plenty of other diamonds in stock that he wants to sell.

So then you take the diamond to another jeweler, are disappointed by his offer, and begin to wonder if you had been cheated. The simple fact is that you, as the consumer, cannot buy a diamond at retail and expect to resell it at the same price to a dealer who buys at wholesale. This is not only true of diamonds but also of nearly any other commodity you can mention.

Then, too, it must be remembered that the taxes you've paid on the ring cannot be taken into consideration for resale value, and that the setting, which has been used, has lost much of its value.

However, there is one consolation. Long after the $3,500 automobile and the $1,000 coat are forgotten and valueless, the diamond can still be sold anywhere in the civilized world for cash, even though it may not be as much as you paid for it.

The other side of the investment story is that large diamonds—2 carats and up of high quality— have increased substantially in value in a relatively short time. When I started in the jewelry business in 1925, top quality diamonds of 3 carats retailed at between $2,500 to $3,500. Today such diamonds are priced from $9,000 to $10,000, and are difficult to find.

The price of diamonds from ¼ carat to 2 carats has remained fairly stable over the years, as shown in the accompanying chart. The figures indicate the range in retail prices for loose diamonds of various sizes. The range from low to high is due to the qual-

ity of the stones. This chart was compiled by De
Beers in consultation with representative jewelers.

	¼ Carat	½ Carat	1 Carat	2 Carats
1949	$90—210	$255—490	$655—1175	$1500—3400
1950	85—205	215—445	520—1090	1200—3120
1951	85—195	220—475	570—1195	1260—3205
1952	85—180	215—425	585—1135	1250—3115
1953	90—195	215—440	570—1180	1280—3190
1954	85—195	200—435	605—1175	1355—3265
1955	85—190	220—450	590—1180	1275—3245
1956	85—215	200—445	540—1170	1295—3300
1957	90—215	210—470	570—1180	1340—3175
1958	95—225	215—485	605—1210	1370—3350
1959	90—220	220—465	560—1240	1540—3455

Price plus tax

Suddenly, however, in 1960, Europeans entered the
market as never before, buying large fine diamonds
which brought the price of the finest stones up materially in sizes of 1 carat and more.

Witness this quotation as of January 1963:

¼ Carat	½ Carat	1 Carat	2 Carats
$70—250	$150—515	$420—1590	$800—4250

At the lower end of the scale, prices are below those
shown in the chart. This is because the scarcity

of quality diamonds resulted in stones of inferior grades being added to jewelers' stocks.

The most significant increase took place among best quality stones of 1- and 2-carat size. In March, 1963, De Beers announced an increase of 5 percent in the price of diamonds in the rough. In 1964 there was an additional 10 percent added, and it is likely that the upward trend will continue. By September 1964, the quotation on finest quality 1-carat stones had climbed to $1,750, and for 2-carat stones to $5,500, and larger sizes in proportion.

Some of these price increases can be attributed to the fact that European buyers are actually outbidding Americans on the New York wholesale market. Part of this, of course, is a reflection of Europe's booming economy, but some observers consider this buying to be a hedge against possible currency devaluation.

In this respect, Europeans are much more realistic about diamond purchases than Americans. Americans buy diamonds—for sentiment, pleasure, gifts, or financial well-being. Not so in Europe where these gems are frequently purchased for protection against unstable governments and currencies. Just before and during World War II, thousands of persons were able to escape Hitler's Germany and from his advancing armies only because their diamonds yielded ready cash or provided attractive bribes. Many

Cubans were able to flee Castro and start a new life elsewhere with the help of their diamonds. More recently, the unprecedented world demand for diamonds has extended to the Orient where the Japanese are buying them for the first time.

De Beers empire has given diamonds a worldwide price stability. For this reason, if for no other, the syndicate has proved its worth. Since the total value of gem diamonds is many billions of dollars, any sudden drop in their price would have worldwide repercussions. This has happened at least twice—in the 1750s when the Brazilian fields were opened up, and in 1869 when the first large discoveries were made in South Africa.

Well, then, should one buy diamonds as an investment? Yes. But only if you are in a position to diversify substantial wealth.

I think most economists would agree with me that in the United States, with its great stability, nothing can take the place of gilt-edged bonds and stocks as long-term investments. We are not likely to have to make a swift exit with quickly negotiable assets for political reasons. So diamonds become an attractive investment only if you have an adequate portfolio of securities, ample insurance, other solid investments, and are looking for further diversification in such commodities as objets d'art, sculpture, paintings, fine musical instruments, and the like.

If you are in this category, buy diamonds for investment by all means, but buy only diamonds of excellent quality and color. In the long run these have proven to be the best from the intrinsic standpoint.

The story of Diamond Jim Brady is a case in point. Although he owned thousands of diamonds, he was more interested in size than color and quality. Thus, when his estate was settled, the value of his diamonds was much less than the price he paid for them.

The best sizes from an investment angle would be diamonds from 1 to 3 carats, because they will always find a ready market, if a quick conversion to cash is required. Larger diamonds, up to 10 carats and over, will always have their intrinsic value, but are more difficult to sell quickly. It is like trying to get a $100 bill changed, compared to a $5 or $10 one.

Loose diamonds are best to buy for investment. It is frequently possible, when buying several diamonds, to work with a jeweler on a commission basis.

CHAPTER 12

Diamonds and I

"Mysterious are the ways of
dames and diamonds . . ."

—Anonymous

In the sense that there are times when he must not reveal all he knows, a jeweler is somewhat in the position of a priest or psychiatrist. I know of jewelers who unwittingly let the cat out of the bag and precipitated a domestic crisis by asking a simple, civil question like this: "How did you like that diamond pin your husband bought last month?"

Unless she is wearing the pin, or mentions it first, it's safer not to mention it at all. It may have been purchased for a third party.

This sort of thing doesn't happen just among the well-to-do. Once, when I was a young clerk in a jewelry store, I had a shoe repairman casually buy an inexpensive piece of costume jewelry. That chore done, he sat down and with infinite care selected a beautiful gold diamond set locket; lockets were the rage those days. The costume piece, he said, was to be mailed to his wife, and the diamond piece to his girl friend. I suppose he felt he had to send his wife something in order to ease his conscience. He was obviously a little hesitant about my youth, as he warned, "Be sure you don't get them mixed."

I have learned over the years that it is not at all unusual for men to buy trinkets for their wives while at the same time they purchase something more expensive for another woman. I am not implying, of course, that wives ought to be suspicious whenever husbands buy them some unexpected bit of jewelry.

You might think that a jeweler runs a dignified, unexciting kind of business. Actually, he encounters a wide cross-section of humanity, with its bewildering mixture of foibles and nobility, and there is something about a jeweler's showcase that reveals the truth about a person's character.

Once, a well-dressed rancher came in with a woman who apparently had been his companion of the previous evening. It was evident she had come in to pick out the diamond watch he had promised during the warm glow of their companionship; a glow that seemed to have faded somewhat in the light of day.

He wanted her to settle for a modestly priced watch. She insisted on an expensive one. Their discussion grew louder and more profane as I stood by helplessly. Suddenly she was struck with inspiration. She looked at me and asked, "Will you take out the difference in trade?"

Another incident which happened in the early days of my jewelry career concerned a customer who wanted to see several loose diamonds. He wanted to surprise his wife with one, and she would come in later to pick out the setting. He wished each diamond taken out of its little paper folder, so he could compare them. Eight diamonds were on the table and I had counted them carefully. He had a fountain pen out, and he kept taking off the cap and putting it back on over and over. Suddenly, I counted only seven diamonds. I left him and the stones, went to the front door, closed it, and had one of the clerks call the proprietor. The man subsequently admitted that with sleight-of-hand, he had snapped one of the stones into the cap of the pen, which we found later had a sort of greasy substance at the base of the cap. Thus I learned firsthand about diamonds' affinity for grease.

I suppose every jeweler has had someone try to switch stones or rings, and I am no exception. Some

THE FASCINATION OF DIAMONDS

ago a man showed great interest in a large dia-

years ago a man showed great interest in a large diamond. After examining it closely he left, promising to come back. He did. In his pocket was a ring, set with a worthless stone but in a mounting resembling the one in our stock. Had it been a small stone he might have succeeded, but it was large enough for me to detect. Switching rings is an old game, but we are always learning of new and clever variations of the art.

I remember the sweet-faced old lady who kept dropping her handkerchief on different rings she took out of a tray. She said she couldn't make a selection unless she had several out to compare simultaneously. Each time I picked up her handkerchief for her, it would come down on another ring. It is a risky business accusing anyone like this of larcenous intent. I just had to outwit her at her own game.

The confidence fraternity also plies its trade at the diamond counter.

Once I had a phone call from a lady who identified herself as a customer. She was going to a party that evening, and wanted to purchase a new diamond bracelet for the occasion. She would send her chauffeur in that afternoon, and if I would give him three or four, she would select one. She was assured that this would be fine.

A liveried chauffeur presented himself later that day, said he was sent by the lady described and did

I have a package ready for him? A sixth sense made me ask him to wait a minute, as I wanted to call the customer, just to be sure. She knew nothing about it, and the "chauffeur," who suspected what I was doing, quietly left while I was at the phone.

One of my treasured memories concerns a man who purchased an inexpensive diamond pin, stating that he had a mania for anything with diamonds. He gave me a check and asked me to confirm the fact that he carried a substantial bank balance. Two weeks later, he came in again, asked for me, and this time purchased a diamond set pendant. Again he paid by check.

Through the next several months he developed into a good customer, always paying for his purchases. Showing interest in a fine piece one day, he asked me to hold it out, as he wouldn't need it for several days. He insisted on paying a deposit on it, although I assured him that wasn't at all necessary. Several days later, he came in, paid the balance, took the jewelry, and left. Only this time his large check bounced. My sixth sense wasn't on the job that time.

He victimized several local dealers this way, and on the final day he and his bank balance left town hurriedly.

Yes, and diamonds attract the queer ones, too.

One day during the Depression a distinguished-looking gentleman came into our store, mentioned that he was a European nobleman and said that an acquaintance of mine had recommended that he look over our stock.

He examined our diamonds the entire morning, choosing a few, rejecting others. We went out to lunch together and he proved to be a most interesting conversationalist. During the afternoon he resumed his shopping. ''This I must have,'' he would murmur. ''This stone is exquisite. I shall take it also.''

At the end of the day his selections amounted to several thousand dollars. I had never sold such a quantity of jewelry in a single day and I was beside myself with delight. He left, promising to come back the following morning to look over a few more pieces and pay for his purchases.

I telephoned our mutual friend to thank her for sending such a fine customer to the store, and, incidentally, to assure myself that the customer's check would be good.

''Oh dear,'' my friend exclaimed, ''was Alberto in your store?''

My heart sank as she continued, ''No, I didn't send him to you, although we were talking about your store a day or two ago. He is an old friend, staying with us a few days. Alberto is almost destitute, but he has delusions of great wealth. He's harmless, but for goodness sake, I hope you didn't let him take anything of value! He couldn't possibly pay for it.''

Sadly, I put Alberto's selections back into stock. He never came back.

Jewelers well know that the vast majority of people are honest, and these few instances are the exceptions which prove the rule. Innumerable times I have mailed out selections of diamond rings to people in our area for their examination when they cannot come to the store. Not once has any of these persons taken advantage of me.

Indeed, some of these individuals who bought their first diamond by mail visit the store years later, make themselves known, and make additional purchases.

And what veteran jeweler hasn't had the thrill of hearing, "Years ago you sold me my engagement ring. Now I want you to meet my son, and do the same for him." It makes us realize that we are not as young as we were, but it is a thrill just the same.

Taken as a whole, jewelers observe humanity at its best, and this is reward enough for some of the problems that are peculiar to the diamond business. Because of my love for diamonds, I wouldn't trade my problems, even if they were doubled, for those of any other line of endeavor.

I never tire of the thrill of helping a young couple select their engagement and wedding rings. The diamond ring that will seal their engagement is the symbol of a new life together, and the start of a series of exciting, pleasurable, wonderful events—marriage, starting a home, rearing a family. At this happy moment of their lives, the two young people view the world through the rosiest of rose-colored glasses with no thoughts of the problems ahead. To share their bliss vicariously, even if only in a small way, is so rewarding an experience that I cannot help but absorb a little of their happiness.

What excitement it is to watch a bride-to-be try on her ring, so full of emotion that her hand trembles. And the groom, as excited as she, but concealing his emotions beneath the veneer of bravado, so familiar to jewelers, as he slips the ring on her finger. This is one of life's greatest moments for the pair, and we are privileged to share it with them. Sometimes the starry-eyed look of adoration on the girl's face is so intimate, so personal, that I make it a point to leave the sales room so as not to intrude on a moment so sacred to them.

Unfortunately not all young couples are like this. I have seen them bickering over the selection. I have seen members of families accompany the pair, taking a strong position against the wishes of one or the other, and it is obvious there will be rough going ahead for the couple.

After many years a jeweler fancies himself, however erroneously, a judge of human nature. He thinks he can tell which marriages will be happy and successful, and which will be shattered by selfishness, immaturity, or outside interference. Like most dedicated jewelers, I am a sentimentalist, and I sincerely hope that the diamonds purchased at my store will have a happy story to tell.

So universal is the appeal of diamonds that often I am privileged to help older, single ladies select some for themselves. Many times I have heard them say: "I guess I'm one of those who will never have a diamond purchased for me, so I'll have to buy one myself if I am ever to have it. I am not going to miss out on the joy of owning a diamond."

Middle-aged men, after achieving some financial success, frequently buy their wives a larger and more beautiful stone than the one they could afford at the start of married life. Their story is a familiar one: "I couldn't afford to give her much of a diamond when we became engaged, but I resolved to get her a larger one when I could, and here I am."

Sometimes the original stone is traded in on a larger one. Often, however, the wife refuses to part with it. The diamond in her worn old engagement ring is too full of happy memories. Sometimes she has it mounted in a pin or pendant.

Then there are the elderly ladies who come to buy themselves a diamond ring after their children are grown. Running through their stories is a familiar theme: "My husband and I had quite a struggle putting our children through school, and we were never able to afford a nice diamond. Now the children have their own families and my husband is gone. He left me a little money and I want to buy the ring he had hoped to get me."

Diamonds do indeed have a magic about them.

CHAPTER 13

Getting the Most for Your Money

The study of diamonds is not easy. When they are first taken from the earth, they are divided into hundreds of different categories. The cutters then shape each individual stone, give each its fire and luster, and play a large part in establishing the ultimate price of the gem.

When a diamond weighing 1 carat finally reaches the consumer, it may be priced at anywhere from $100 to $2,000. The wide difference, of course, is due to variations in quality.

Four factors are involved in determining the value

of a diamond, and three of them have to do with quality, namely: clarity, cut, and color.

There are wide variations, too, in each of these factors, which have been made even more confusing by ambiguities in terminology, so that the average layman is completely at a loss to understand their real meaning.

The fourth factor is weight, or carats, and for obvious reasons, the size of the stone must be considered.

In the final analysis, however, the best guarantee of getting proper value for the money spent on a diamond is to buy the stone from an established and reliable merchant, because he has devoted many years to building up the knowledge and a good reputation, which are his greatest assets. He will be the first to tell you there are no bargains in diamonds. But he will also be able to help you get a full measure of value for the money you spend.

Since even those who have made a study of diamonds know so little about them, it is easy for the casual buyer to receive less than he pays for. In buying from an unknown source, you are apt to be victimized by any number of misrepresentations, including the matter of whether the stone is really a diamond. There are no simple rules which can be used as a yardstick.

A diamond may be roughly compared to currency. With a little training, you can usually tell genuine dollar bills from counterfeits, and by the same token you can distinguish a diamond from a bit of bottle glass. But even bank tellers, who handle money constantly, take in counterfeit bills occasionally. And so it is with diamonds.

I could tell you that diamonds have a specific gravity of 3.52, but you wouldn't have the proper scale to check it, and even if you did, you couldn't check a mounted stone by this test. Besides, even the gravity test isn't infallible because some glass has the same weight. I could also tell you that the diamond is single refractive but so are some other transparent stones.

Diamonds are the hardest known substance. They will cut glass, but so will certain other gems. You could, of course, try to scratch a questionable stone with a known diamond. But if the specimen is indeed a diamond, you could very well ruin both stones, and this could be a very expensive test. But no reliable dealer would dare represent a lesser stone as being a diamond, so at least this problem is eliminated when you make your purchase from a reputable merchant.

Diamonds are very special objects. They deserve to be selected with very special care.

What CARATS Mean to a Diamond

Diamonds are bought and sold by weight, and weight is involved in the price of a stone at every stage—from the mine to the retail jeweler. The weight is measured in carats, but until 1910 a carat in one country was not necessarily the same as in another. That year, an international congress of weights and measures agreed that 200 milligrams (0.007 ounces) would be one carat. The United States adopted this standard in 1913.

The carat was divided under the decimal system into 100 points. Thus, a stone weighing exactly 1 carat was 100 points. A ½-carat stone would then weigh 50 points. The weight of a stone of 1½ carats would be written 1.50 ct. A simple rule is to think of this in terms of dollars and cents; there being 100 cents in a dollar, a 1½-carat stone would therefore be shown as 1.50.

Few stones weigh precisely 1 carat, or ½ carat. Even though in practice many jewelers advertise their stones as weighing "about one-half carat" or "approximately one carat," each point is worth money and you are entitled to know exactly what you are getting.

A diamond approximated at ½ carat may turn out to be only .42, and is worth correspondingly less. Many dealers make it a practice to note the exact weight of the stone on the sales slip. If this is not done, you would be wise to request it.

Diamonds are not measured lineally, but a 1-carat stone of average cut is about ¼ inch in diameter.

The illustration below will give you an idea of the relative sizes of stones up to 2 carats.

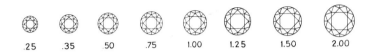

.25 .35 .50 .75 1.00 1.25 1.50 2.00

The larger the diamond, the more rare and costly it is. On the average, only one rough diamond large enough to produce a finished 1-carat stone of gem quality is found for every 250 tons of diamond-bearing material processed. The ratio of gems to rocks and earth is much greater for diamonds of larger sizes. It is obvious why the larger the diamond, the more it costs per carat. Thus, a 1-carat diamond is worth more than 2 diamonds weighing ½ carat each. A ½-carat diamond (50 points, or 50 one-hundredths), is more costly than 2 stones weighing 25 points each, provided the quality is the same. Here, of course, diamonds may no longer be compared to currency.

If you should see an advertisement for a ½-carat diamond, showing a stone almost as large as a dime, it is well to assume the illustration has been distorted to show details of the mounting. Otherwise, you will be badly disappointed when you see the actual diamond.

Merchants often advertise a ½-carat ring for some

ridiculous price, and add in very small type that this is the total weight of all the diamonds in the ring. In reality the center stone may weigh only 30 points, with 4 small stones in the setting contributing to the total of 50 points. Remember, the difference between one stone weighing ½ carat, and 5 stones weighing a total of ½ carat, is important. Be sure to ascertain the exact size of the center diamond as this is where your money goes principally; the small stones are worth much less per carat.

Therefore if a ring is shown you described as "This is our Princess Abigail Model" at only $150, let us ask the weight of the Princess, at least as far as the center diamond is concerned.

The only time this principle does not apply is when a wedding band, studded with several small stones, is being purchased. The total weight of the gems in this case is important only relative to price, determined by quality.

How CLARITY Affects a Diamond's Price

Clarity has to do with the diamond's internal quality—the imperfections or the absence of them within the stone. Few diamonds are flawless. In stones weighing more than ½ carat, 99 percent have some internal imperfection.

These flaws, called inclusions, may vary from a tiny white spot very difficult to see with magnification, to large and numerous flaws. They may be transparent (white) or colored. All such imperfections, created when nature made the stone, lower its value. The more noticeable the inclusion, the greater its effect on the value.

An infinitesimal white spot lowers the value the least. The larger and more numerous the flaws, the more they affect the diamond's value.

It is your privilege to examine a diamond the same way the jeweler does—under his 10-power magnifying glass called a loupe. While some of the smaller inclusions may escape your untrained eye, you may see others that could not be spotted without the glass. Any reputable jeweler should gladly be of assistance in helping you to see whatever inclusions are present.

The various types of inclusions go by a variety of names. Here are the most common:

Carbon spots—these occur most frequently. They appear to be black and range from a tiny speck to quite large and numerous ones.

Bubble—a transparent, roundish inclusion which may be tiny or large. These are actually small im-

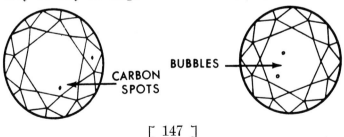

bedded crystals or grains of a different material.

Clouds—a group of tiny transparent spots that give the stone a slightly clouded appearance.

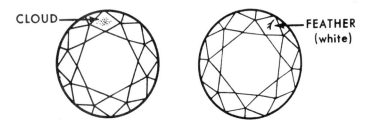

Feathers—transparent inclusions that occasionally take the appearance of a feather, although other shapes may be included in this category. Some jewelers refer to all transparent inclusions as feathers. Large feathers may be serious cracks in the stone.

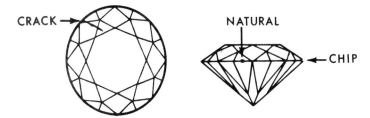

Cleavage crack—a crack in the stone along a line of cleavage (the grain of the stone). Such a flaw may affect the durability of the diamond. This brings us to a point worth mentioning: though a diamond is the hardest material in the world, it may be chipped or broken if given a sharp blow against a hard object. While this doesn't happen frequently, it can occur if the stone is hit in a cleavage direction. A diamond has direction where it can be split; like a piece of wood, it must be cut along the grain. While accidental damage to a stone isn't likely, a diamond should be handled carefully.

Natural—a pit or blemish on the outer edge (or girdle) of the stone. This is part of the original surface of the rough stone, left by the cutter to avoid excessive weight loss. If the natural is tiny, and confined within the width of the girdle, many competent diamond graders do not class it as an imperfection.

Chip—a flaw created in the handling of the stone. This is not a true inclusion in that it is not a natural imperfection, but they occur often enough to be mentioned. A chip is usually on the edge of the stone.

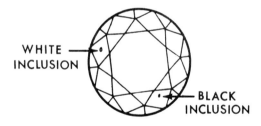

Position of the inclusions (or imperfections) should be considered. A spot in the center of the stone would impair the value more than a similar one near the edge, where it would not be so easily seen.

What is a flawless diamond?

The Federal Trade Commission has ruled that no diamond may be called ''flawless'' unless it discloses no flaws, cracks, spots, carbon spots, blemishes, or imperfections of any kind when examined loose by a *competent* observer using a 10-power magnification. Few gems can pass such a test.

Is there such a thing as a ''perfect'' diamond? The Federal Trade Commission's rule is that the stone must not only be flawless, but it must be properly cut and proportioned, and must be of good color. The finest jewelers adhere very strictly to this standard.

The general brilliance and beauty of diamonds are not affected by inclusions unless they are large enough to be seen by the naked eye. Cut and color, to be discussed later, have much more to do with a stone's beauty than minor inclusions. The point to keep in mind is that even though inclusions do not mar the appearance of a stone, the tiniest imperfections lower its value compared to flawless gems.

There is no standard system at present of classifying diamonds according to the extent of their imperfections. Some jewelers designate a flawless stone as zero. A stone with a very minute inclusion would be classified 1, a slightly less perfect gem would be 2, and so on.

Another jeweler might use letters A, B, and C. Many use the terms VVSI (very, very slight inclusion, or very, very slight imperfection); VSI (very slight inclusion); SI (slight inclusion or imperfection); and Imperfect, which would cover a wide range of flaws.

Actually, these private classification codes are quite arbitrary and do not mean a great deal provided you ask about the flaws and the jeweler points them out to you.

Now don't be alarmed if told that your diamond is not flawless. By far most of the gems being worn are not. It is just that flaws or imperfections affect value as far as clarity is concerned.

If possible to examine the stone loose, before it is set, this is to your advantage. A tiny inclusion which may be seen when the stone is loose might not be visible when it is set. Many jewelers show diamonds loose; however, for economic reasons if no other, the average jeweler can't afford to carry both a loose and mounted stock.

You may be startled at the variation from one dealer to another of what is told you, but after you have looked at a few diamonds with a 10-power eye loupe or magnifier, you will start forming opinions of your own.

A misleading term used occasionally is "eye perfect." The connotation is of fine quality, but its real meaning is that the stone is flawed but not to the extent that the inclusions can be seen by the naked eye. The best jewelers frown on this term. Diamonds should never be graded this way. Another ambiguous term is "90% or 95% perfect" or whatever percentage the jeweler chooses to classify it.

Also beware of the boast, "Our very finest quality," used in some so-called "wholesale" diamond catalogues. The chances are their "very finest" may be nowhere near as fine as the finest quality carried in your retail jeweler's regular stock. All these terms are relative, and the only real test is in a careful, personal inspection.

Above all, don't be hesitant about asking questions when shopping for a diamond. After all, you don't buy diamonds every day and you are entitled to find out all you can before making a purchase. If a jeweler showing you stones displays a disinclination to answer your questions clearly, he may be trying to conceal vital information. In any case, it's time to try someone else.

What CUT Does for a Diamond

A diamond cutter improves on Nature by taking a rough stone and, by precise cutting and shaping, giving it the brilliant fire that makes it the most prized of all gems. A skilled cutter can bring out every possible bit of the beauty which nature built into the stone. A less skilled cutter, given a stone of similar size and quality, might fail to develop it to its full potential.

Thus, of the four c's of diamond value—carats, clarity, cut, and color—the factor of human skill enters only into the cutting. Even though a diamond is flawless internally and its color superb, only skillful cutting can bring out its maximum beauty. Precision is the goal in this art, and to achieve it every facet must be symmetrical; its angles must not vary by more than a half degree from the ideal.

In practice, there are two meanings to the word cut. One, of course, is the verb, meaning the proportioning, faceting, and polishing which we have been talking about. The other meaning is that of the noun, referring to the shape into which the stone has been fashioned.

Six of the most popular cuts, or shapes, are shown in the illustrations that follow. There are many others, used as embellishments in the mountings.

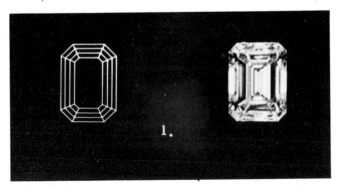

No. 1 is called the emerald cut. It is distinguished by the rectangular style top face, or table.

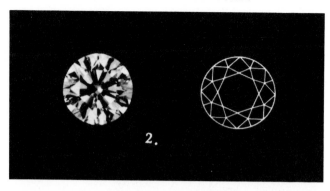

2.

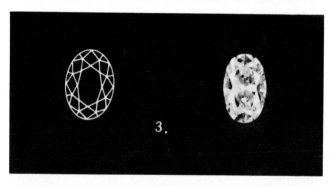

3.

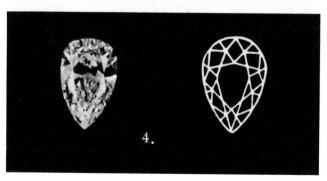

4.

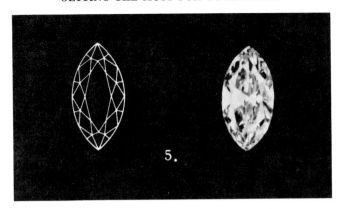

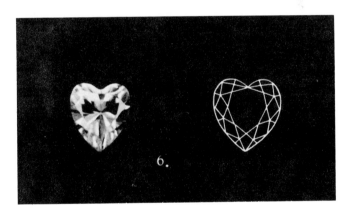

No. 2 is the round, also called the brilliant. The round has the greatest glitter.

No. 3 is oval.

No. 4 is pear-shaped, sometimes called pendeloque.

No. 5 is the marquise (pronounced Mar KEYS), also boat-shaped.

No. 6 is heart-shaped.

 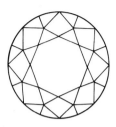

When light enters a properly cut diamond, it is reflected from facet to facet and comes back through the top of the stone in a brilliant rainbow blaze.

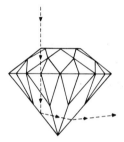 

In a stone that is too deep, much of the light is reflected to opposite facets at the wrong angle to return through top of diamond and is lost through the sides.

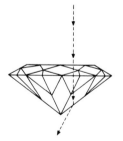 

In a shallow stone, much of the light is lost, as it fails to be reflected at all and "leaks" out at the bottom.

[156]

The shape into which the stone is cut depends primarily on its shape in the rough. While a stone is cut to bring out its brilliance, it must also be remembered that flaws must be eliminated, and the cutting done with the least loss to the stone's weight.

Since the round, or "brilliant," diamond is the best known, the comments that follow regarding the faceting of stones will apply primarily to that shape.

To understand the "why" of cutting, it is necessary to know that a diamond is a light trap and light concentrator. The stone must be cut so that rays of light, striking the various facets and entering the stone, are reflected out through the top in highly concentrated form. The more of this light that is focused up through the top, or table, the more brilliant the stone will be.

Cutting has another function. It brings out the diamond's power of light dispersion, or its ability to separate the white light entering the stone into the many colors of the spectrum. A well-cut diamond sends back to your eye a dazzling array of brilliant rainbow hues.

At this point, it might be well to review some of the terms introduced in Chapter 4 and present a few new ones.

Facet—one of the many flat surfaces, or faces, cut into a stone.

Table—the stone's largest face, at the top; in round diamonds, an octagon.

THE FASCINATION OF DIAMONDS

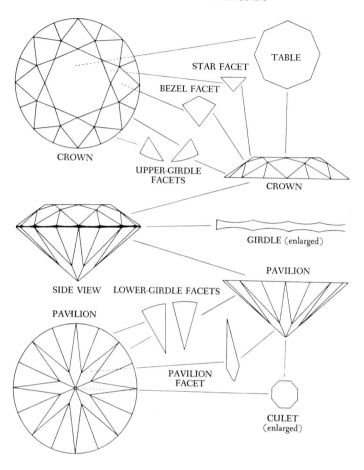

Girdle—the extreme outside edge of the stone.
Crown—that part of the stone above the girdle.

Culet—the small face at the very base of the stone.

Make—a diamond's "make" refers to the correctness of proportions, the finishing and polishing, the symmetry, the correct placing of the facets at the proper angle—in other words, the skill of the cutting job.

Finish—the excellence of the polish, the smoothness of the girdle; the culet.

The full-cut diamond is distinguished by the fact that it has either 57 or 58 facets or faces. There are 32 facets plus the table above the girdle—a total of 33. Below the girdle (the pavilion) are 24 facets, plus the culet if there is one. Some stones are cut without the culet.

Each of these 57 or 58 faces must be properly placed, sized, and angled to achieve the greatest brilliance. It has not been proven that the addition of facets above this number improves the stone. However, in exceptionally large stones, more than the usual number of facets may be used. The Cullinan, for example, has 74 facets.

Very small diamonds—in the 1, 2, and 3 point sizes and smaller—are generally cut with only 17 facets. This is called the *single cut*. There are 8 facets plus the table in the upper half, and 8 in the lower half. Diamonds of the smallest size, 1 point and smaller, are sometimes cut with the full 57 facets, but when they are too small such stones take on a slightly fuzzy appearance. Stones of 3 or 4 points (.04 ct.) or larger should be full cut for maximum brilliance.

The *American cut* is an additional term that should be explained. It refers to a precise mathematical formula for bringing out a high degree of brilliancy and fire. American gem cutters developed this formula, and hence its name. The term is used for this particular formula, regardless of where the stone is cut.

The American cut calls for the table to be 53 percent of the stone's diameter. The crown should be about one-fourth of the depth of the diamond and the lower part about three-fourths. The total depth should be 60 percent of its diameter. The girdle must be very thin and exactly horizontal and parallel to the table. Each facet must be symmetrical and properly placed, the culet tiny or nonexistent. The finish must be of the highest order.

Very few diamonds are cut exactly to this standard. Those that are fall in the most expensive brackets. However, stones that do not vary far from these proportions can still be very beautiful.

What is the best shape to buy? This is a matter of personal choice. The round has always been, and always will be, the most popular.

In the large sizes, around 5 carats and over, emerald, pear, oval, or marquise are preferable. To many women, these other shapes are preferred in any size. This is entirely a matter of taste. The round, when properly cut, is the most brilliant, but while the brilliancy of the others is lessened to a varying degree, their beauty in appearance makes up for it to countless people.

Emerald-cut diamonds are from 20 to 30 percent lower in cost than round diamonds in sizes up to 2 carats. Then the prices of these two tend to become more even until they get to 6 or 7 carats in size. Then the emerald cut overtakes the round in price.

Generally, oval and pear shapes cost about the same as the round. Marquise-cut diamonds run quite a bit more than round diamonds, provided they are well cut and proportioned. This is due to the fact that there are fewer stones which lend themselves to this type of cutting, and because more rough is lost in cutting a marquise than the others.

In order to achieve its highest potential, any style of cutting, whether it be emerald cut, pear shape, oval, marquise, or any other, must adhere to strict standards, just as the round or brilliant cut. For example, if the table of an emerald-cut diamond is very large, taking most of the entire top of the stone, as it often does, the value is lessened. Approximately one quarter of the stone should be above the girdle, and three fourths below, to have an ideally proportioned gem.

Most cutters have integrity. But as in all professions, there are some cutters who don't hesitate to take advantage of every trick known to the trade, and there are many tricks. In addition there is the element of skill. Just as some doctors are better surgeons than others, some cutters are more competent than others.

Some of the more common errors in cutting diamonds include cutting stones too thick or too shallow, resulting in loss of brilliancy and fire. Some have greatly enlarged tables, making a very spread stone; here also beauty is sacrificed. Girdles are often too thick and wavy, or not parallel to the table. Occasionally a brilliant-cut stone is out of round. Sometimes an extra facet may be seen. Facets exceeding the usual number in a cut diamond are the result of polishing away a chip, natural, or nick. This should be considered a factor in a lowering of a diamond's value. Almost all these faults are the result of the cutter's desire to retain maximum weight.

Having read something of what constitute the qualities of a well-cut diamond, beware of the term "perfect cut," which is often loosely and incorrectly used. A perfectly cut stone is encountered less frequently than a flawless diamond. Caution should be exercised when this term is encountered.

When a salesman explains that the diamond is perfectly cut because it has 58 facets, it means absolutely nothing. If you are told that a certain 2-carat diamond looks like a 3-carat stone, that would be the very reason why you shouldn't buy that one. A 2-carat stone of good proportions should look like a 2-carat stone and not a 3-carat one.

In looking at two or more diamonds of the same size, you may discern a slight difference in their brilliancy. This would be due to cutting. Examine them, remembering brilliance and sparkle, and, as far as cutting is concerned, take the one which looks best to you.

Most diamonds found in a reliable establishment are well cut, and though you will seldom see the paragon described earlier, the ones to avoid are those which deviate so much from the standard that the diamond loses too much brilliancy and life, thus sacrificing beauty.

A beautifully cut diamond is a fine example of how man's knowledge and skill have been applied to one of nature's wonderful creations to achieve infinite beauty.

COLOR and Value

Given two diamonds of equal weight and clarity, would the cut or color be the more important factor in establishing its value? There are many jewelers who think that cutting is the more important. Good cutting is most essential to a diamond's beauty as explained in the preceding chapter.

My own opinion is that good color is far more desirable than good cutting if a choice must be made, and it certainly has more bearing on the diamond's value.

A poorly cut stone can, if it is large enough, be cut again. But there is not much that can be done about faulty color, although efforts have been made to alter even this characteristic.

Color is of such importance that if two diamonds, each weighing a carat, each superbly cut and proportioned, and each flawless, were to be compared, a difference in color might result in one stone being valued at several hundred dollars more than the other.

Diamonds are found with tints of pink, blue, green, canary, and other hues. Even though these stones are cherished because they are so rare, the white, or colorless stone, is most beautiful in my opinion. However, there are as many as 200 shades of white diamond, which makes color grading difficult, indeed.

The finest colorless diamond might be compared to a drop of distilled water—totally without color except for the rainbow hues it flashes as it separates the light spectrum.

Color evaluation is such a tricky matter that it should be attempted only with the use of a colorimeter, an instrument called a Diamondlite, or a similar apparatus. The Diamondlite provides an arti-

The author using a Diamondlite.

ficial light equivalent to the light that enters a north
window on a clear day. The gem to be checked is
placed under the light and compared to a series of

[165]

standardized gems of known color. North daylight is used because it has a constant wavelength.

Direct sunlight with its rays of varying length flatters a diamond and it is impossible to determine a diamond's true color under such conditions. If your jeweler lacks a color-grading instrument, view the diamond in the light from a north window on a cloudless day. Always examine the stone from the side: any yellow content is more noticeable than when you look straight down into the stone.

Practically all diamonds have some yellow or brown tint. Diamonds with a very slight degree of yellow are very beautiful and valuable stones, equally brilliant as the whitest; but the rule is—the less yellow, the finer the quality, and the more valuable the stone.

As in the cut and clarity of stones, the absence of absolute standards has led to unfortunate and misleading terms being applied to color. I am sure you have heard the expression ''blue white'' applied to diamonds. Some jewelers use it only to describe the finer grades of diamond color. Others use it with reference to stones with a discernible yellow content. Extremely few diamonds have any blue body color in them.

Thus, ''blue white'' can mean almost anything and it is useless in describing a diamond. Here are some other terms to beware of. Stones that are ''over-blue'' turn out to be somewhat brown under artificial light. ''Commercial white'' has the implication of fine white color, but it is another meaningless description avoided by ethical jewelers. ''Top silver cape'' is used on stones that have color, but look white when placed in a setting.

Only when diamonds are unmounted may their true color be accurately judged. Many jewelers show their diamonds loose, for the reason that a prospective customer may examine them under the best conditions; however, as previously stated, the average jeweler just can't afford both a loose and a mounted stock of diamonds.

A good trick is to breathe on a diamond. This sometimes tends to bring out a yellow tint that otherwise wouldn't show up, if indeed there is some yellow in the stone.

Diamonds reflect the color of their surroundings, so don't look at a diamond under a jeweler's blue lamp.

Diamonds are sometimes artificially whitened to increase their value, but it has been found that such stones revert to their original shade after a time. In some states, the law requires that such stones be so identified when color has been altered.

Diamonds can also be given a green, gold, or other hue by exposing them to irradiation in a cyclotron. These colors are permanent, but the stones lose some of their brilliance in this process. Only diamonds of poor color are irradiated as no one would try to improve the color of a fine white stone.

Personally, I have never seen a colored diamond, artificial or natural, which was as intensely beautiful as a colorless diamond, with its ability to sparkle, and pick up all the colors of the rainbow.

Color, more than a diamond's other attributes, affects value so much that again, if at all possible, buy from a reputable merchant of integrity. His colorless diamonds will remain colorless forever.

CHAPTER 14

The Important Questions
About Diamonds

How should I buy a diamond?

The answer is: Go to a reputable dealer. This is
your surest protection. Even at reliable stores, if you
don't have one where you do your buying without
question, you will find a variance in values. Some
have more overhead expense, and have to charge
more. If you inquire the price of a finest quality 2-
carat diamond from several fine jewelers, no two will
have the same price. There is no standardization in

[169]

the retail prices of diamonds. What you have learned in this book will make shopping for your diamond more fun. You will gain greater enjoyment from the stone once you purchase it. And it will help you buy the diamond that is best for you.

It takes years to become an expert in any field, and diamonds are a particularly difficult subject to master. As I have pointed out, every slight variation in clarity, cut, and color affects the price of any diamond. Only the most experienced dealers can be sure of their judgment when evaluating a stone.

What is the best diamond to buy?

The best diamond is the diamond that is best for you. This depends on how much you can wisely invest.

For those who can afford the finest, remember *clarity, cut,* and *color.* If you want the best, the stone must be flawless, the cut and proportions exact, the color clear without a hint of yellow or brown tint. A stone with all these characteristics will be expensive, but ownership of such a gem will give you the pride and satisfaction of possessing a perfect specimen of nature's greatest jewel.

Most persons will settle for something less. A diamond of good color and cut, having only minor inclusions, will give you a fine, sound stone representing excellent quality. For the same expenditure, you will be able to purchase a somewhat larger stone in this category than in the one described in the preceding paragraph. Keep in mind that very small inclusions will affect the beauty of a stone less than inferior color and cut. In summary, buy the finest stone you can afford. You will make no mistake by following this rule.

What should I look for in choosing a stone?

In brief, look for beauty, brilliance, and fire. Only an expert can evaluate the placing of the facets and their angles, but some of a stone's shortcomings will become visible to you if it is compared with other diamonds. Examine several stones at the same time.

Examine the stones from the side. Is the girdle on a straight line and parallel to the table? Are the table and culet lined up properly?

Look at the stones from the top. Is the table disproportionately large? If it is, it may fool your friends into thinking you have a big and costly stone, but its real value would be open to question.

Look at two or more diamonds of the same size, and you are likely to detect a slight difference in their brilliance. This would be due to the cutting. Take the one that looks best to you.

It's well enough to say go to a reputable dealer, but what if I'm not quite certain about the jeweler I'm doing business with?

There are no more honest and ethical merchants than those who deal in diamonds. At the same time there are no greater misrepresentations than those offered by sharp or outright unethical diamond dealers who take advantage of the public's lack of knowledge about diamonds. If you aren't sure about the merchandise you are being shown, look around. Make comparisons.

Chances are, after reading this book thoroughly you will know more about diamonds than the untrained salesman who characterizes the store where ethical standards are somewhat less than the highest. If the sales clerk is vague, or he gives you answers that contradict what you've learned here, it's time to do your diamond shopping elsewhere.

What is the possibility of buying diamonds wholesale?

Legitimate wholesalers of diamonds sell only to the retail dealers. They do not sell directly to the public. Their merchandise goes to the jewelry trade and is not distributed indiscriminately to everyone.

You can be sure that so-called wholesale houses which sell to the public do not sell at true wholesale

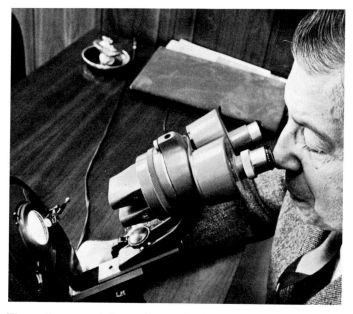

The author examining a diamond with binocular microscope.

prices. The merchandise advertised in the catalogues available to the public should be carefully scrutinized. The prices listed as your "wholesale" cost are usually no lower, and often higher, than the retail prices of legitimate dealers who buy directly from the cutters and who expertly grade their own stones. The "retail" prices listed in these catalogues are almost always inflated.

Once again, shop around. Compare values and see for yourself.

Well, isn't there a chance of buying diamonds at a bargain during a "sale" or in a discount house?

There are few, if any, bargains in diamonds. You rarely get more than you pay for.

There's a diamond "sale" going on almost all the time in any large city. The merchants who consistently advertise such sales are likely to have their goods marked too high in the first place, and it is quite possible their "sale" prices are no lower than the every-day price of dealers who don't have sales.

High pressure sales tactics are designed to take advantage of the average person's unfamiliarity with diamonds. Not long ago a New York store advertised "flawless, finest quality" 1-carat stones for $600. The legitimate wholesale price for such gems was considerably higher. Examination of the stones on sale revealed them to be imperfect specimens. Explained the manager of the store: "It is simply a difference of opinion between experts in a highly technical business." Perhaps so, but you don't want to be caught on the short end of such a difference of opinion.

Don't "guaranteed" diamonds protect you?

A guarantee is only as good as the firm that issues it. Among my souvenirs is a "Diamond Guarantee Bond" issued by a certain cut-rate jewelry firm. A

0.53 ct. diamond ring was purchased at "wholesale" from this firm for $350, and the "guarantee bond" accompanied the stone. The quality of the center diamond is listed as "AA," whatever that means. The diamond had some important imperfections, and an approximate retail value of $275. I suppose if the owner of the stone were dissatisfied with his purchase, he could have taken it back along with the guarantee—and the money he spent would have been applied toward the cost of another over-priced, inferior stone. What good is such a guarantee?

Could I get diamonds at a cut price from loan firms and at stock liquidation sales?

If this merchandise was as good as most of these people say it is, they wouldn't have to go to the expense of advertising. Any number of jewelers would snap it up.

Could I get a good deal from a private party?

You might, if you are buying from a friend you can trust who is willing to sacrifice his diamond for quick money. But both of you would be wise to have the stone appraised by a competent jeweler. Not all jewelers do this work. The appraisal fee will be well spent, no matter how it comes out, and you will still be friends.

[175]

Photograph by Charles E. Grover

Binocular microscope photo of a diamond which was sold as "perfect." Stone was flawless, but cutting job was atrocious.

[176]

But beware of diamonds offered for sale in the want-ad columns. The bargain may be legitimate. On the other hand, there are individuals who make a good living by buying diamonds from jewelers and reselling them to gullible individuals at a fat profit under the guise of distress selling.

Be sure and pick your own appraiser, whether you're considering buying from a stranger or a cut-rate store that urges you to have the diamond appraised "to make sure." There are unethical appraisers just as there are unethical jewelers. It is not unusual for such sellers to send you for an inflated evaluation to an appraiser with whom they are working for an inflated profit.

Can diamonds be bought cheaper abroad?

No. At the wholesale level I have found diamond prices no cheaper abroad than in the United States. In addition, there is the matter of duty when you bring the gems home. And in the case of misrepresentation, there isn't much you can do about getting your money back.

Again, in some foreign countries, the standards of quality are not so strict as in our own. Recently, I had a customer who purchased some large diamonds in South Africa from a licensed dealer who had been highly recommended for his integrity. The diamonds were classified as of the finest quality with no flaws and of top color. He had a certificate stating this. We were asked to appraise the diamonds and mount them in cocktail rings. We couldn't classify them as flawless, and showed a very disappointed man through our binocular microscope what we meant. Now I am sure that the dealers who sold them did so honestly enough; it was just that our standards of flawlessness differed. If that happened in this country, the customer could sue for adjustment, but where the purchase was made thousands of miles away, in a foreign land, an adjustment becomes somewhat difficult, to say the least.

And a word of warning regarding the import tax of 10 percent, applicable on cut diamonds brought into this country. Don't ever forget to declare it, as the seller very frequently advises the customs department of the sale. This is done because a liberal percentage of the duty goes to the informer.

Now that our own 10 percent excise tax on diamonds has been removed, while the import duty still applies, diamonds are best purchased right here at home.

Is the purchase of a diamond always a terribly risky adventure?

An adventure it certainly is, whether you are buying a diamond for your own enjoyment, an engagement ring, a stone for a loving wife who has been your helpmate on the road to success, or a large gem as a long-term investment. But it need not be a risky adventure if you heed the things I have pointed out to you in this book.

And finally, when considering a purchase, take your time. Compare. Ask questions. Look around. And enjoy the experience. You will buy many things in life far exceeding what you spend for a diamond, but none will provide quite the same thrilling and lasting pleasure. A diamond is forever, and you should not be hasty about making such an important investment in happiness.

Index

INDEX

INDEX

INDEX

Prinsloo, Joachim, 90
Producer, largest, 15, 115-116

Rahab, Prince, 112
Rajah of Gwalior, 82
Rajah of Malwa, 82
Rama Sita, 95
Ranjit Singh, 85
Refractive, single, 143
Regent Diamond, 86, 88-89
Rhodes, Cecil John, 65-71, 72
Rhodes, Herbert, 65
Rhodesia, 71
Robert Bruce, 107
Round cut, 155, 157, 160, 161
Royal gems, 53-54, 91, 93, 95, 99, 103-112
Russia, 33-34, 114

Sawing, 38, 45
Scaif, 45
Sea water, effect of on diamonds, 30
Selling experiences, personal, 131-140
Shah Jehan, 82, 99
Shah Rukh, 83
Shah Shuja, 85
Shah Zeman, 85
Siberia, 19, 47
Sierra Leone, 17, 18, 115, 116
"Sights," 74
Single cut, 39, 159
Size, average, 3, 144-145
Smithsonian Institute, 97
Smugglers, 114-118
Société Minière de Bakwanga, 115-116
Sorel, Agnès, 50
Sources, regional, 12-20
South Africa, 14, 15, 20, 24, 47, 65-73, 89-90, 99, 114, 117-118
South African mines (yield), 24, 30

South West Africa, 15, 18
Soviet Union, 19, 47, 72, 114
Stanton, May Bonfils, 111-112
Sullivan, John L., 55
Sultan Baber, 82
Superstitions, 49

Table, 39, 157
Tavernier Diamond, 93, 95-97
Tavernier, Jean Baptiste, 22, 95,99
Taxes, 178
Tests, 12, 52, 55, 143
Thieves, 88, 95, 96, 113-118, 122-123, 133-135
Tidewater Oil, 33
Timur, 85
Tolkowsky, Marcel, 39
Topkapi Sarayi Museum, 109
Top silver cape, 167
Tower of London, 86, 91, 104
Twining, Lord, 104

United States, 20, 47, 48, 79
Unusual uses, 56-57, 59, 61

Vaal River Valley, 15, 65
Valuation factors, 141-142, 153, 163-164
Value, price scale of, 127, 128
Van Niekerk, 14-15
Victoria, Queen, 47, 85

Wearing, early customs, 49-52
Weight, 3, 41, 143-146
Wellington, Duke of, 86
Wells, Fredrick, 89-90
Wesselton, 15, 24
Williamson, Dr. John T., 17
"Window," 41
Winston, Harry, 97, 100, 102
Woyie River Diamond, 17

Yield per ton, 30, 33